Brain-Boosting Lateral Thinking Puzzles

Series Editor: Heather Dickson

Puzzle Writers: Joanna Hooper, Roya Ireland

Additional Contributors: Joel Hilshey,
Ann Marangos, Sophie Stephen

Page Design and Layout: Linley Clode

Cover Design: Gary Inwood Studios

Published by:
LAGOON BOOKS
PO BOX 311, KT2 5QW, UK
PO BOX 990676, Boston, MA 02199, USA

www.lagoongames.com

ISBN: 1902813227

Printed in Singapore

Brain-Boosting Lateral Thinking Puzzles

Introduction

At last, a pocket-sized volume of the world's best lateral thinking puzzles – that is, puzzles that need you to be able to think outside the box in order to solve them.

Beautifully designed and cleverly illustrated to help trick the reader, these lateral thinking puzzles will appeal to everyone.

Divided into four chapters, each puzzle has a score of 1, 2 or 3 points. If you can crack the puzzles within 60 seconds, you can add the relevant points to your score. So, to start, why not try a few puzzles and see how you fare? If you find them difficult, don't despair. Just as going to the gym tones your muscles, doing puzzles trains your brain and builds up your IQ; so the more puzzles you do, the more likely you are to be able to throw logic to the wind and think laterally.

If a casual reader, you can dip into the book whenever you want and do the puzzles at random. But for those of you who need a bit more of a challenge, why not do all the puzzles in one of the four chapters and see how you get on – there is a score card at the beginning of each chapter to help you add up your score.

For the Ultimate Challenge, complete all the puzzles in this Brain-Boosting title and then turn to page 191 to check out your overall score.

If, once you've completed this book, your brain's ready for another cerebral workout, turn to page 192 for details of Lagoon's other Brain-Boosting titles. For more lateral thinking puzzles see Lagoon's Mind-Bending titles.

Contents

Chapter 1

To see individual ratings for each puzzle see under the title of each question. Once you have completed the chapter, turn to page 8, for help adding up your score.

Then turn to page 53 to start chapter 2.

Chapter 1 - Scoring

Puzzle points for correct answer

Winning Ways	**3**	Legal Loophole	**1**
Wild Thing	**3**	Football Crazy	**1**
Corinthian Conceit	**3**	How Many Heaps?	**3**
Square Numbers	**2**	Spare Part	**1**
It's a Sell Out	**1**	Time Warp	**2**
Watergate	**1**	Feeding Frenzy	**1**
April Fool	**2**	Family Photo	**2**
Poor Visibility	**1**	Princess Sophia	**2**
Extra Set	**2**	Missing Link	**1**
Pick 'n' Mix	**2**	Adding Up	**1**
Beach Boys	**3**	Mortal Combat	**2**

YOUR TOTAL

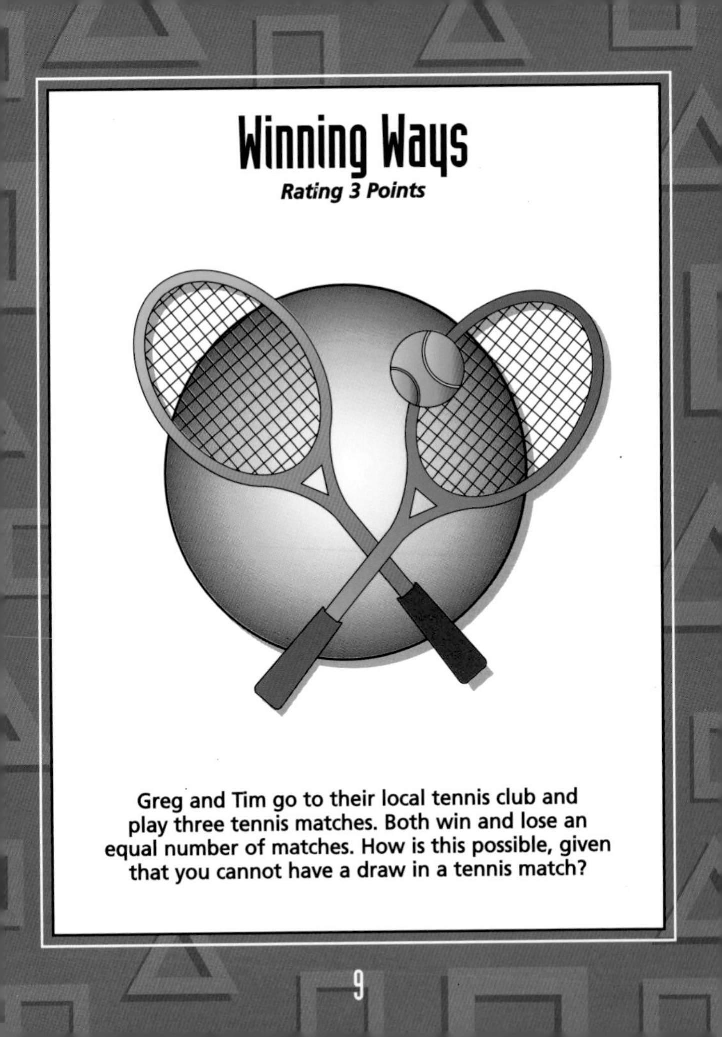

Winning Ways

Rating 3 Points

Greg and Tim go to their local tennis club and play three tennis matches. Both win and lose an equal number of matches. How is this possible, given that you cannot have a draw in a tennis match?

Winning Ways - Solution

They were playing against their girlfriends, not against each other.

Wild Thing

Rating 3 Points

To refresh his senses after a wild party, a man goes out for a walk across a wet and windswept moor. There is low cloud cover and not a single star can be seen in the sky. The man is relatively new to the area and doesn't know the geography of the moor. He has no torch or compass and there is no moonlight to guide his path. How does he avoid getting lost?

Wild Thing - Solution

The man had stayed at the party all night.
It was morning and therefore daylight when he decided to go for a walk, hence he would have no trouble seeing his way.

Corinthian Conceit

Rating 3 Points

Billy is reading about Ancient Greece. One of his history books shows a picture of the remains of a temple in Corinth bearing the inscription 46BC. He looks in another book and sees a picture of exactly the same temple, but on this one the inscription reads AD46. How does Billy know which date is accurate?

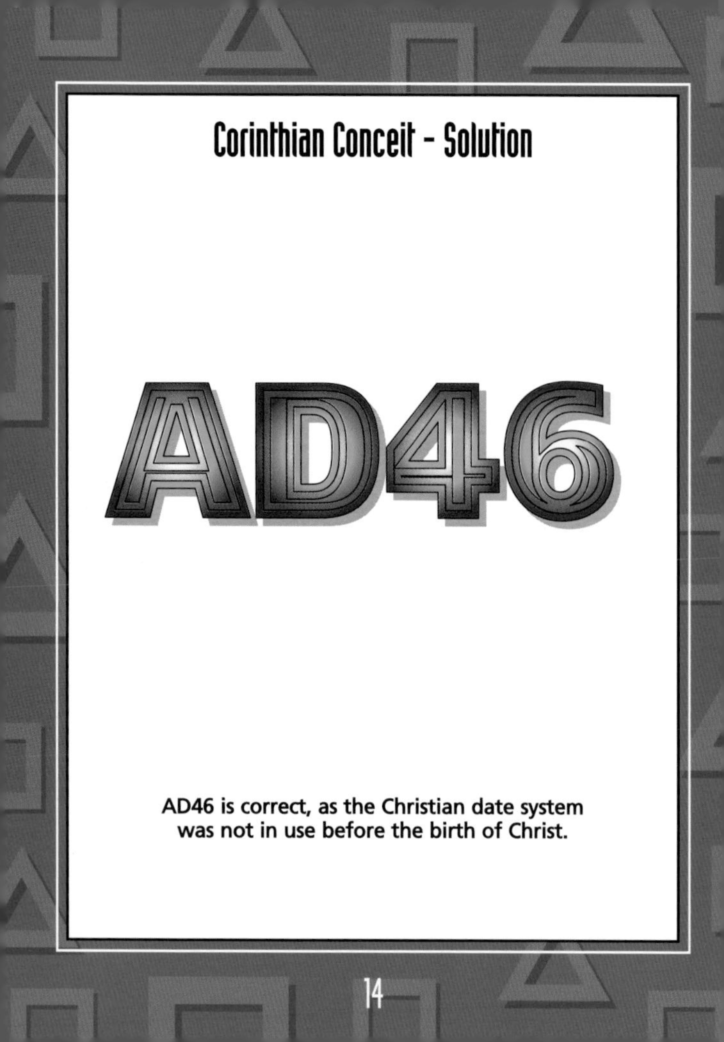

Corinthian Conceit - Solution

AD46

AD46 is correct, as the Christian date system was not in use before the birth of Christ.

Square Numbers

Rating 2 Points

The squares on a board game are numbered consecutively from 1 to 99. In total, how many sixes and sevens are there on the board?

Square Numbers - Solution

1	2	3	4	5	6	7	8	9	10	11
12	13	14	15	16	17	18	19	20	21	22
23	24	25	26	27	28	29	30	31	32	33
34	35	36	37	38	39	40	41	42	43	44
45	46	47	48	49	50	51	52	53	54	55
56	57	58	59	60	61	62	63	64	65	66
67	68	69	70	71	72	73	74	75	76	77
78	79	80	81	82	83	84	85	86	87	88
89	90	91	92	93	94	95	96	97	98	99

40: be careful to note two sixes in 66, two sevens in 77, and one of each in both 67 and 76.

It's a Sell Out

Rating 1 Point

Early one morning a theatre box office sells two dozen tickets at £24 each to an amateur dramatics society whose members all wish to sit in the upper circle. How many tickets at £8 per ticket need to be purchased if the box office is to sell the same number of tickets, for seats in the stalls, that same morning?

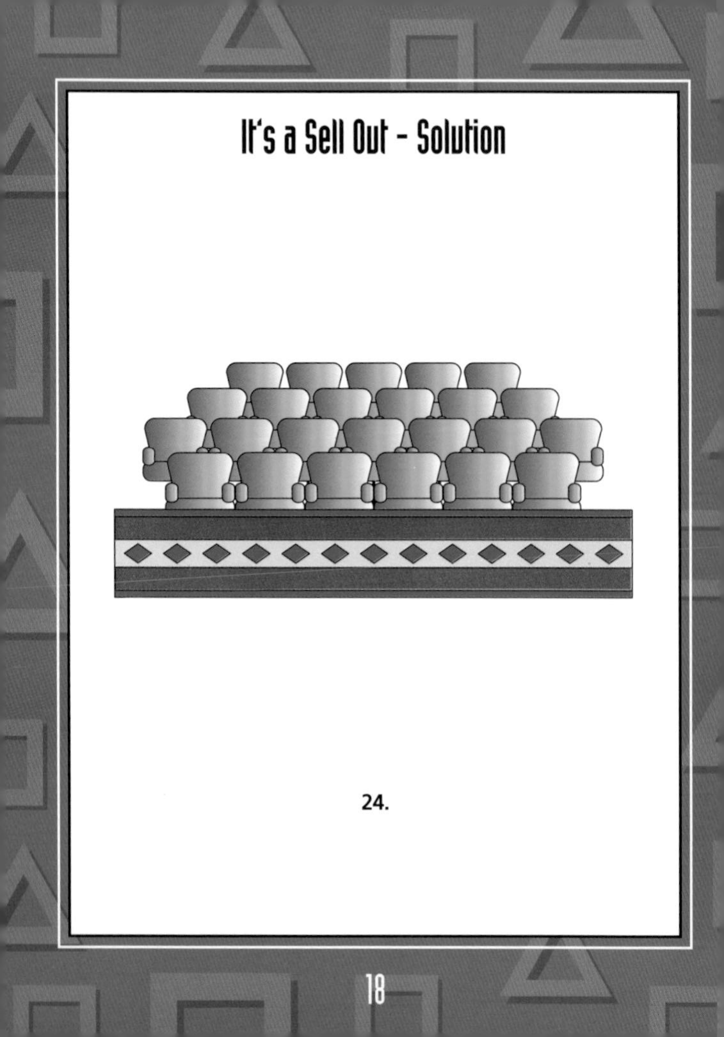

It's a Sell Out - Solution

24.

Watergate

Rating 1 Point

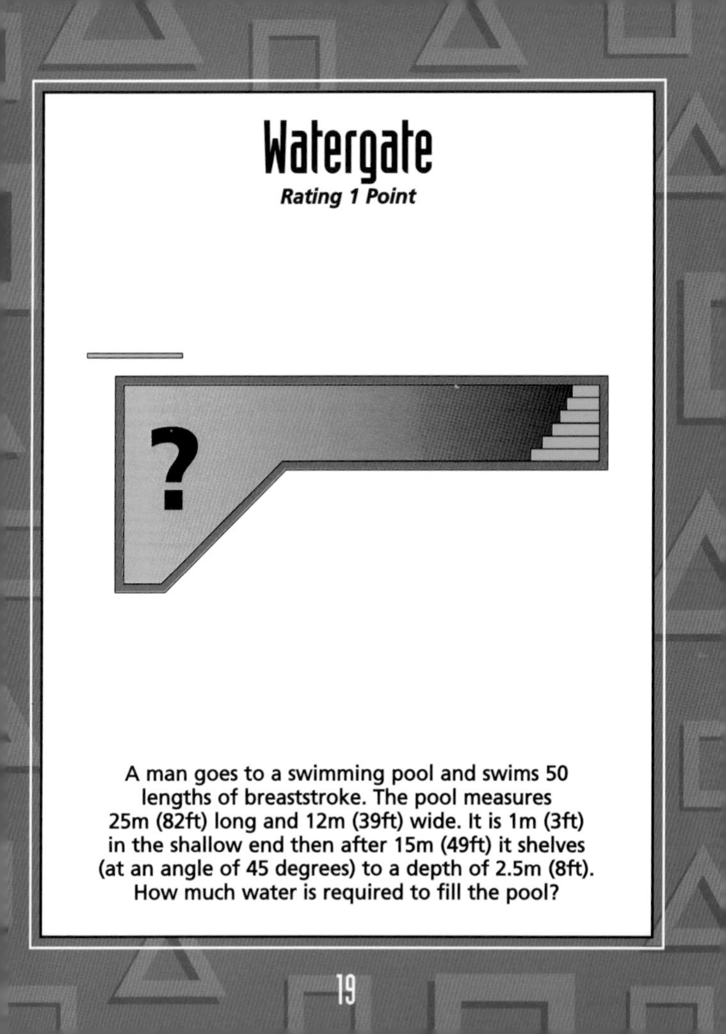

A man goes to a swimming pool and swims 50 lengths of breaststroke. The pool measures 25m (82ft) long and 12m (39ft) wide. It is 1m (3ft) in the shallow end then after 15m (49ft) it shelves (at an angle of 45 degrees) to a depth of 2.5m (8ft). How much water is required to fill the pool?

Watergate - Solution

None. It must already be full if a man has been able to swim in it.

April Fool

Rating 2 Points

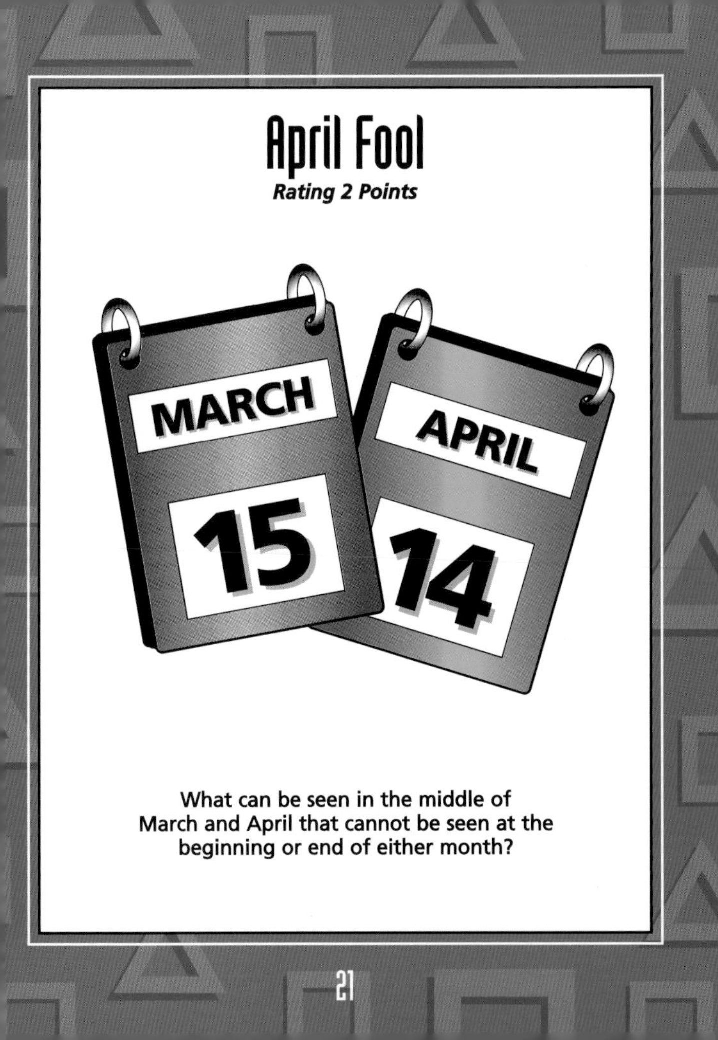

What can be seen in the middle of March and April that cannot be seen at the beginning or end of either month?

April Fool - Solution

The letter 'R'.

Poor Visibility

Rating 1 Point

On the day that President Nixon took office he held his first meeting in a south-facing room at the White House. It was daylight and it wasn't rainy nor was it foggy yet, when he looked out the window, he couldn't see the top of the Empire State Building. Why not?

Poor Visibility - Solution

Because the White House is in Washington and the Empire State Building is in New York.

Extra Set

Rating 2 Points

Mr and Mrs Richardson have two boys who share the same birth date. When they go shopping for their children they always buy three of everything: three pairs of shoes, three pairs of trousers, three shirts, all the same size. The children have no need for lots of spare clothes, so why should they do this?

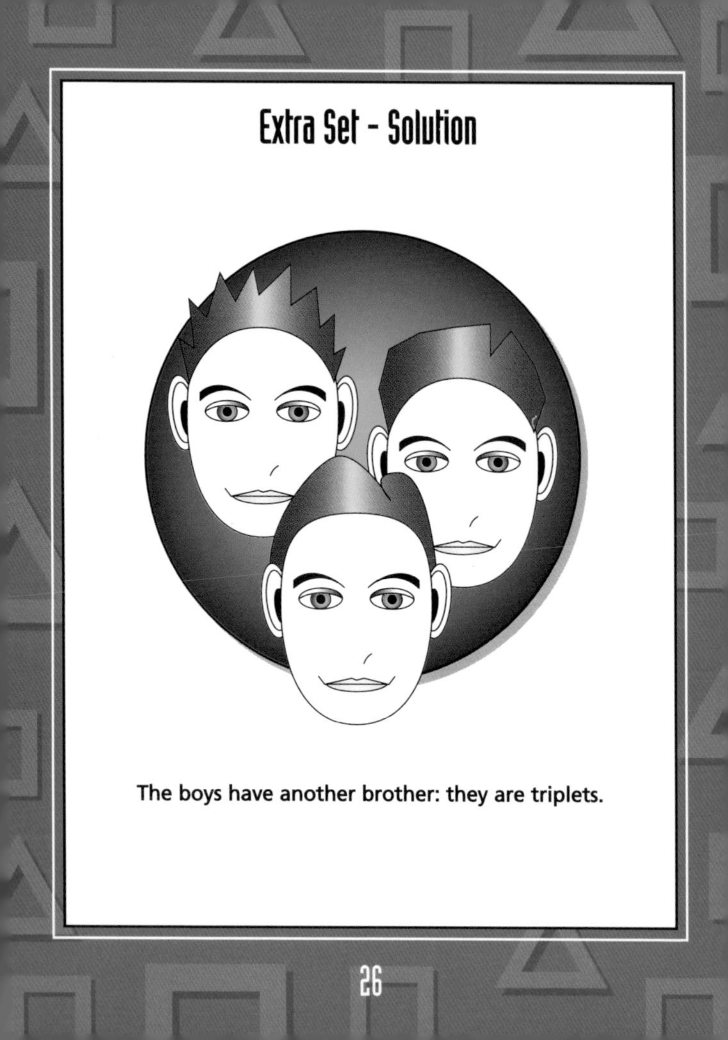

Extra Set - Solution

The boys have another brother: they are triplets.

Pick 'n' Mix

Rating 2 Points

Charlie Chew works behind the pick 'n' mix candy counter at his local store every Saturday. He is a fit and healthy 22-year-old, 2m (6ft 5in) tall, with a size 112cm (44in) chest and size 12 feet. What does he normally weigh?

Pick 'n' Mix - Solution

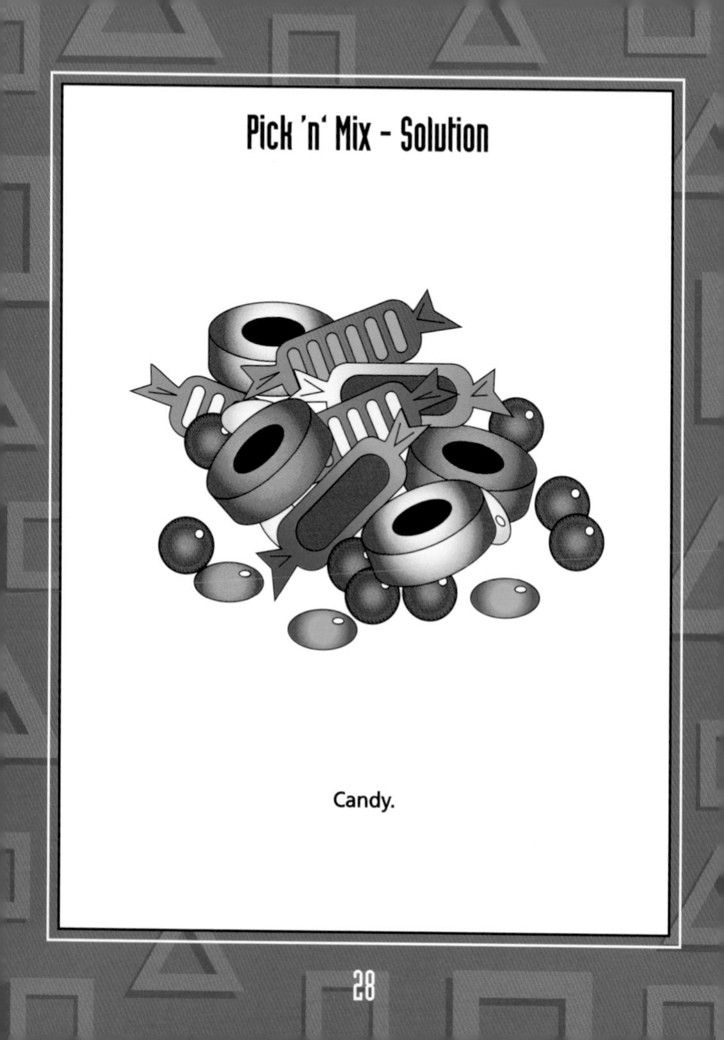

Candy.

Beach Boys

Rating 3 Points

Two seven-year-olds, Keith and Alan, were building sandcastles on the beach. Once they had had enough, they lay down on their backs for an hour on the sand. After a sleep in the sun, they got up to play a game of football. Keith's back was covered in sand, but Alan's back was perfectly clean. Why then did Alan go and wash himself in the sea, while Keith was content to stay on the beach?

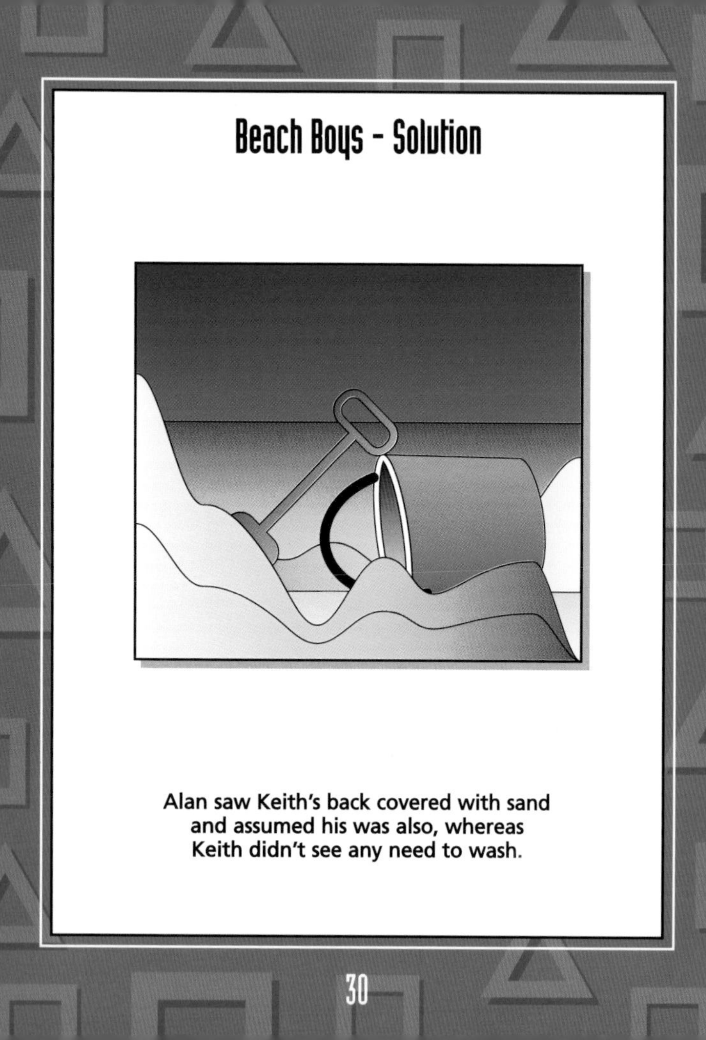

Beach Boys - Solution

Alan saw Keith's back covered with sand
and assumed his was also, whereas
Keith didn't see any need to wash.

Legal Loophole

Rating 1 Point

A French-owned jet carrying forty British tourists home from Sicily crash-landed on the border between Northern Italy, France and Switzerland. Legally speaking, where should any survivors have been buried?

Legal Loophole - Solution

Survivors are not buried.

Football Crazy

Rating 1 Point

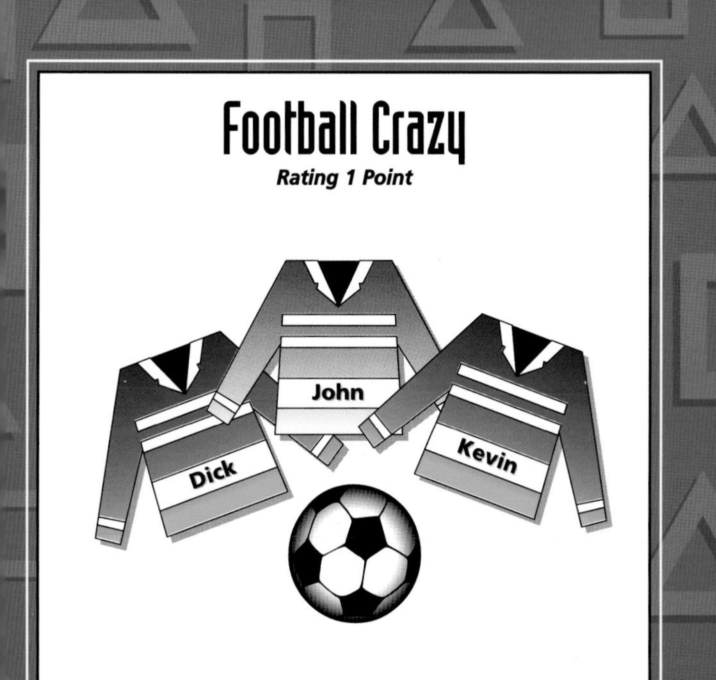

You are refereeing a football match between two teams, the Red City Rovers and the Blue City Wanderers. Four of the 22 players on the pitch are called Kevin, one in the red team and three in the blue team. Three of the players are called Dick, two in the blue team and one in the red team, and both goalkeepers are called John. What is the referee's name?

Football Crazy - Solution

Whatever your own name is,
since you are the referee.

How Many Heaps?

Rating 3 Points

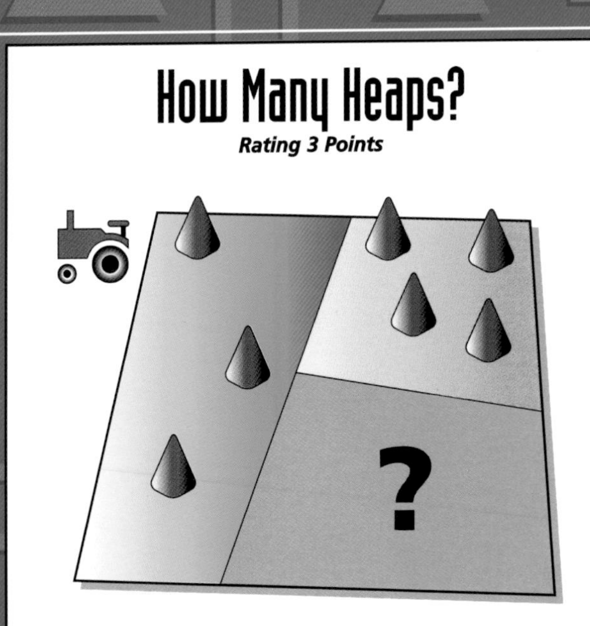

Big Ron is using his tractor to transport manure from his cowshed into two of his fields. After working all day he has created four heaps in his barley field and another three in his wheat field. There is so much manure in the cowshed that the following day he moves the same amount into each field again. How many piles of manure will he end up with if, on the third day, he puts all the heaps from the barley and wheat fields together in a third field?

How Many Heaps - Solution

If he puts all 14 heaps together
he will end up with one large pile.

Spare Part

Rating 1 Point

At a DIY evening class the instructor passes around a box in which there are ten screwdrivers, one for each person present, including himself. Everybody takes a screwdriver, yet there is still one left in the box. Explain.

Spare Part - Solution

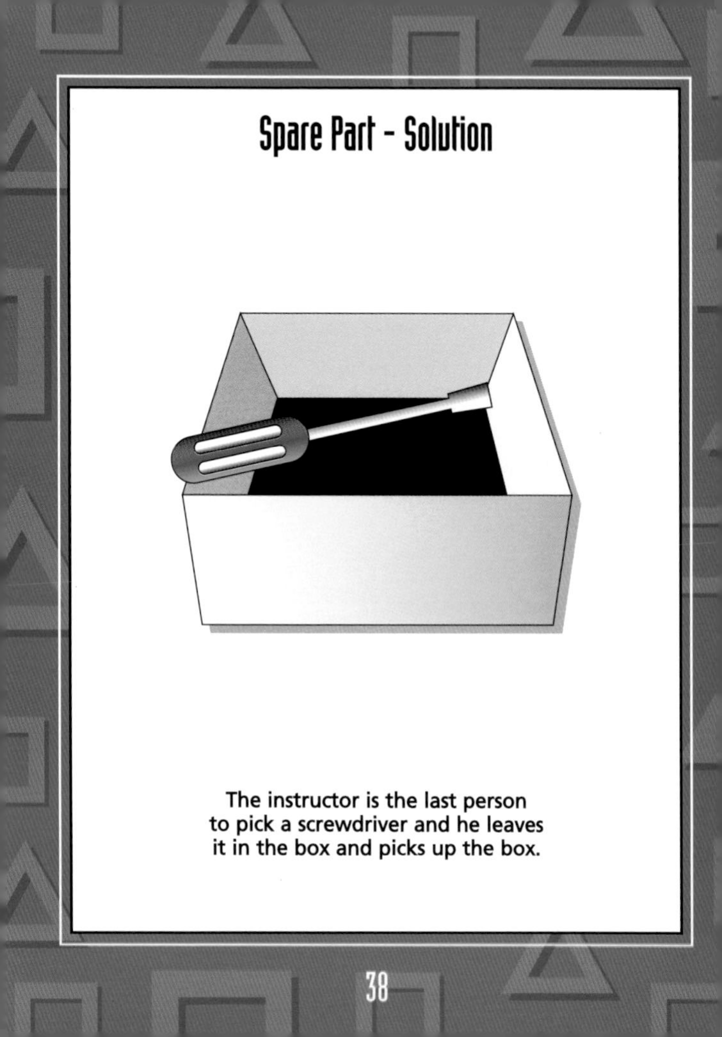

The instructor is the last person
to pick a screwdriver and he leaves
it in the box and picks up the box.

Rating 2 Points

Henry goes cross-country running every Saturday morning after he has had a shower, shaved and had breakfast. He always follows exactly the same route, which takes him 85 minutes from start to finish. One Saturday morning, feeling slightly hungover, he forgets to shave but goes out for his run along the usual route. This time it takes him an hour and twenty-five minutes. Why is this?

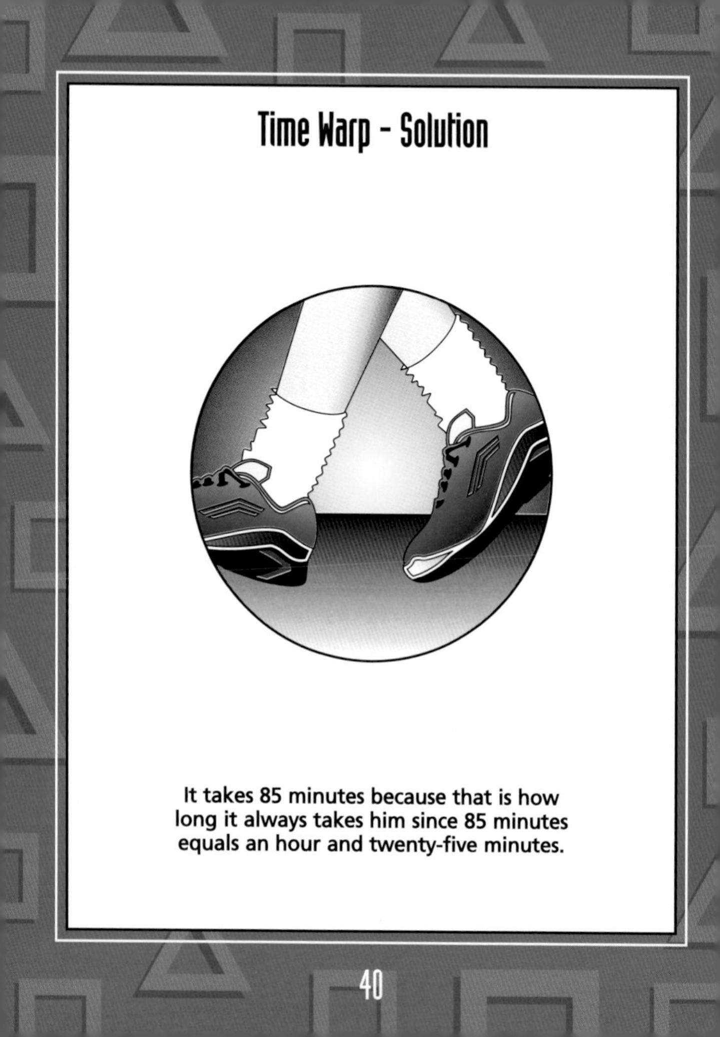

Time Warp - Solution

It takes 85 minutes because that is how long it always takes him since 85 minutes equals an hour and twenty-five minutes.

Feeding Frenzy

Rating 1 Point

Is it more correct to say "The herd of sheep is eating hay in the field" or "The herd of sheep are eating hay in the field"?

Feeding Frenzy - Solution

Neither. The correct terminology is a *flock* of sheep.

Family Photo

Rating 2 Points

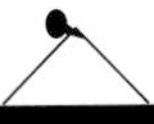

Mr and Mrs Simpson, their two daughters and a niece are waiting outside a photographic studio for another member of their family before having their family portrait taken. A man walks past and both Mrs Simpson and her niece greet him simultaneously, "Hello, father!". Explain.

Family Photo - Solution

The man is a priest.

Princess Sophia

Rating 2 Points

How can Princess Sophia be a one-year-old and nine months old at the same time?

Princess Sophia - Solution

She is a racehorse.

Missing Link

Rating 1 Point

Three brothers called Trevor, Andrew and Robert are sitting in a room. In walks little Oliver, Andrew's nephew. Oliver is neither Trevor's nor Robert's nephew. Explain.

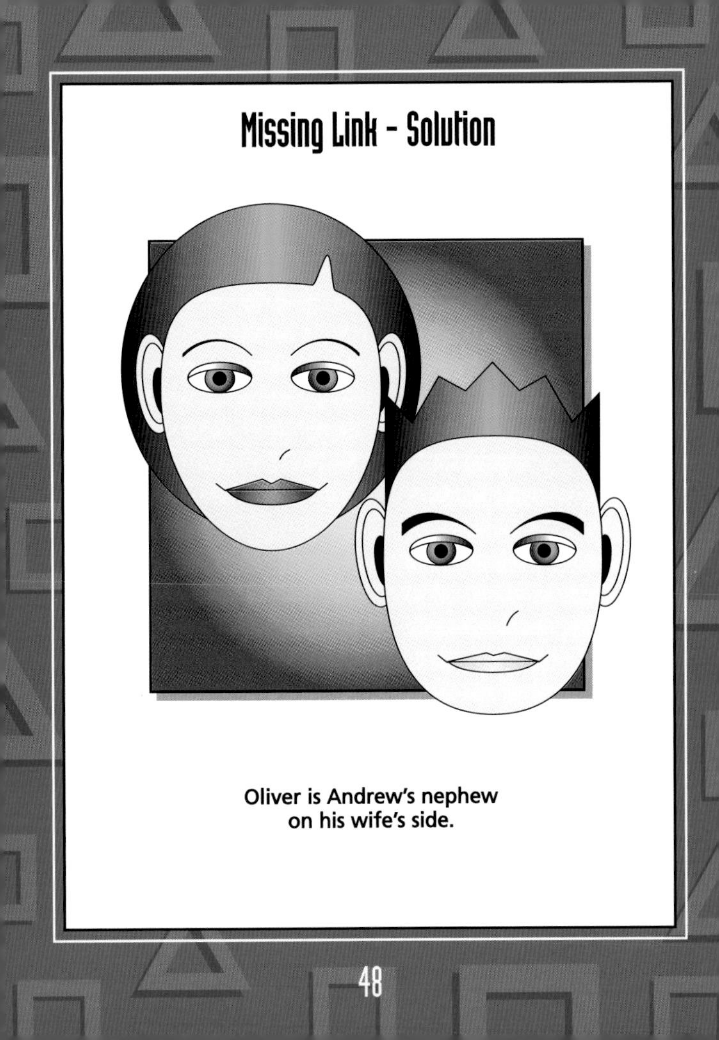

Missing Link - Solution

Oliver is Andrew's nephew
on his wife's side.

Adding Up

Rating 1 Point

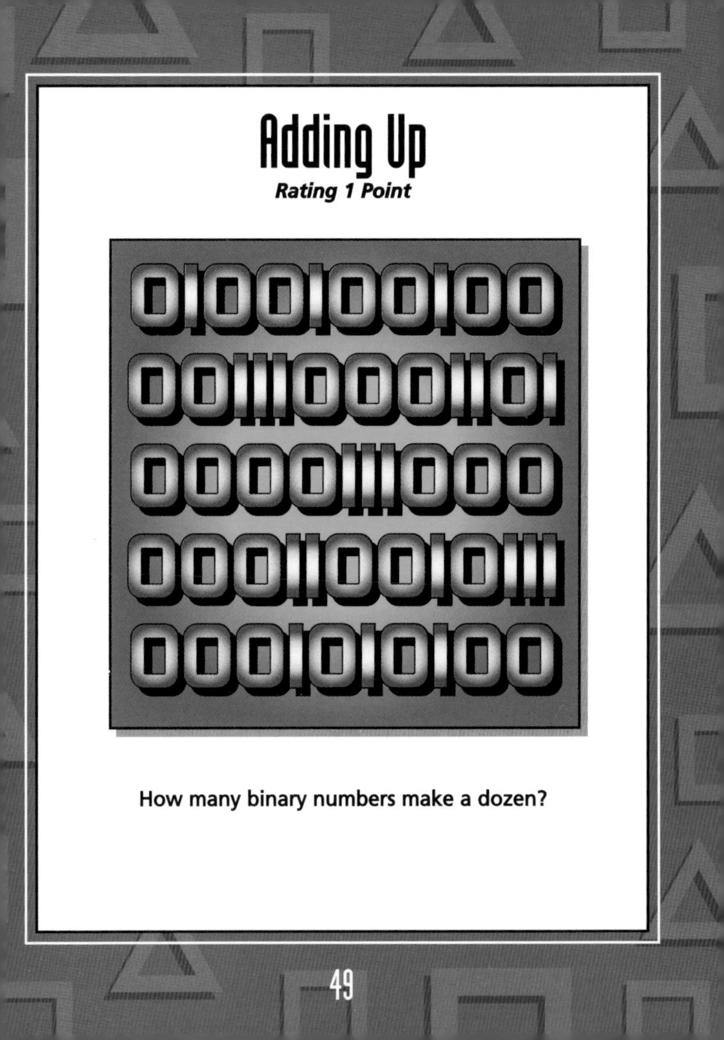

How many binary numbers make a dozen?

Adding Up - Solution

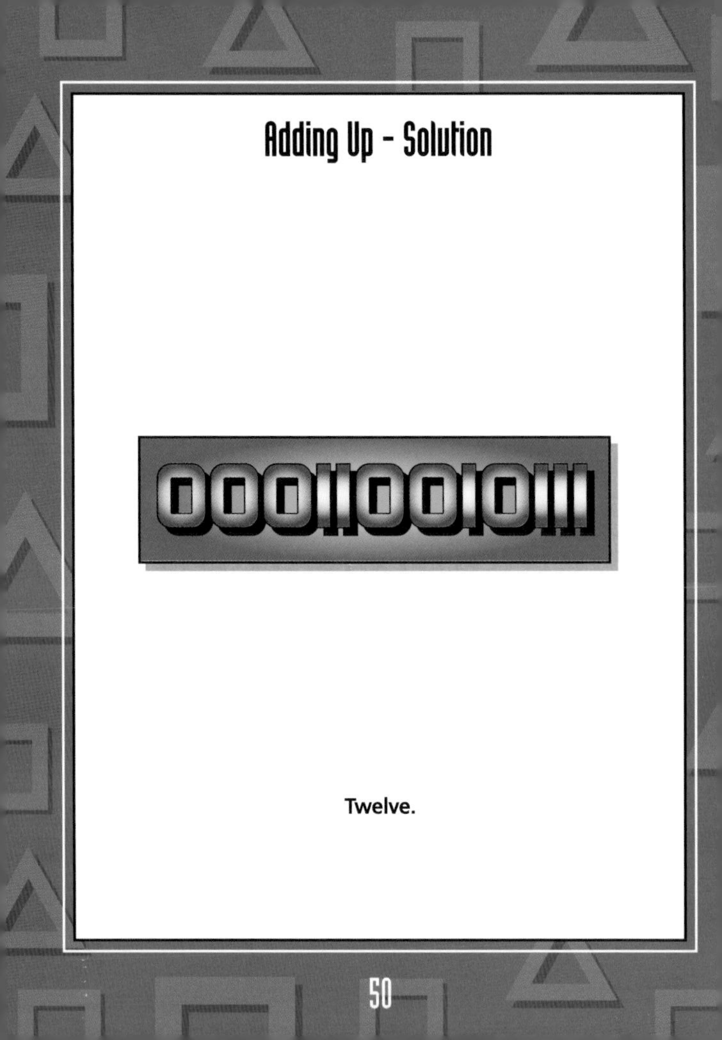

Twelve.

Mortal Combat

Rating 2 Points

Two judo experts take a bow and the match begins. One is wearing a brown belt and the other a black belt. After a long tussle, the black belt judoist has the most points and is declared the winner, despite the fact that throughout the entire contest no man threw the other to the ground. Explain.

Mortal Combat - Solution

The two judoists were women.

Chapter 2

To see individual ratings
for each puzzle see under the
title of each question.

Once you have completed the
chapter, turn to page 54, for
help adding up your score.

Then turn to page 99
to start chapter 3.

Chapter 2 - Scoring

Puzzle points for correct answer

Tempting Offer **3**

Insomniac **2**

Dare Devil **2**

Backbreaker **2**

Animal Magic **3**

Dangerous Driving . . . **2**

Lovers' Tiff. **2**

Family Reunion **1**

Room Temperature Test **1**

Rising Tide. **2**

Last Legs **1**

Room with a View. . . . **1**

Egg Flip **2**

Nightmare Scenario . . **3**

Sales Slump **1**

Small Change **2**

Light Work **3**

Auch Aye the Noo. . . . **2**

Trivial Pursuits **1**

Parent Trouble **1**

Phone Formula **1**

A Question of Strength **2**

YOUR TOTAL

Tempting Offer

Rating 3 Points

Legend has it that a rich but wicked man once offered a poor beggar an earthenware jug containing a sweet-smelling liquid that the wicked man swore would turn everything it came into contact with into pure gold. Why was the poor beggar not deceived?

Tempting Offer - Solution

If the wicked man had been telling the truth,
the earthenware jug would have turned to gold.

Insomniac

Rating 2 Points

A man is awake night after night without getting a wink of sleep, yet he doesn't feel tired. Why?

Insomniac - Solution

He is a night-shift worker
and sleeps during the day.

Dare Devil

Rating 2 Points

Edward bets Richard $10 that he can jump from a ten-storey building to the concrete street below and somehow escape injury. How did Edward manage to be $10 better off?

Dare Devil - Solution

He jumped from a ground floor window.

Backbreaker

Rating 2 Points

Slightly unsteady under the load, a farmer places two 25kg (55lb) bags of apples over his shoulders and carries them to his truck. The bags of apples are to be taken into town to be sold. The farmhand carries three bags. Who is the stronger?

Backbreaker - Solution

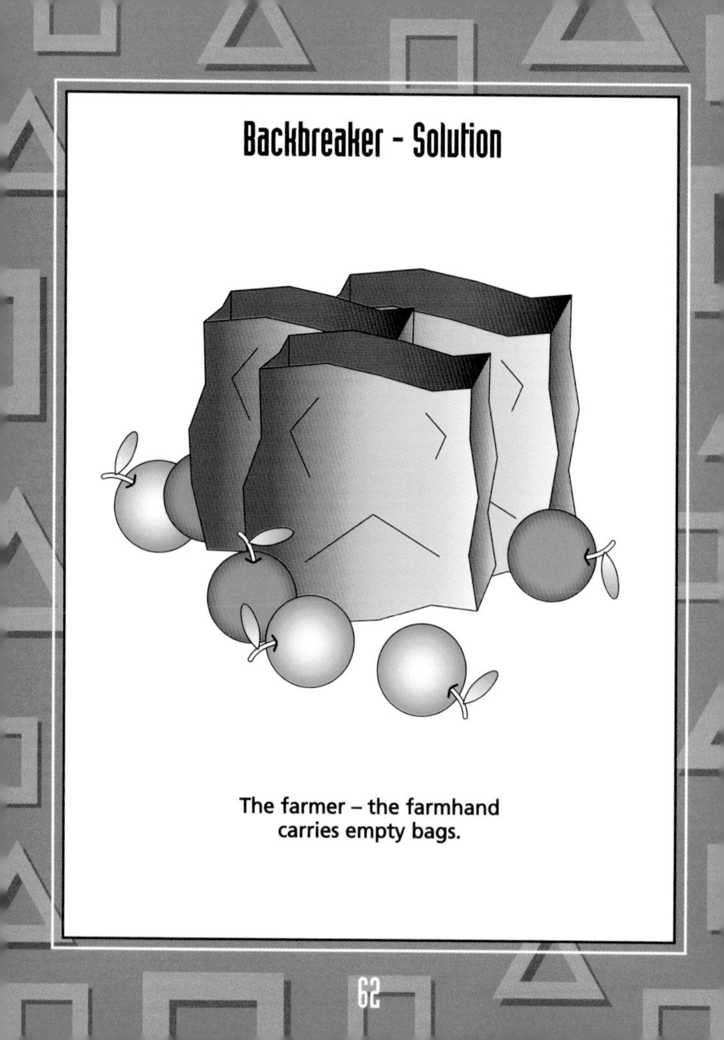

The farmer – the farmhand
carries empty bags.

Animal Magic

Rating 3 Points

A year ago Farmer Brown put his five horses and five donkeys in the same field to save space. No other animals had access to the field and so the horses and donkeys were able to graze together undisturbed. Two days ago Farmer Brown took all the horses to fresher pastures. There are now six animals left in the field. Only five of them are donkeys. How can this be?

Animal Magic - Solution

The other animal is a mule, a cross
between a horse and a donkey,
offspring of the original animals.

Dangerous Driving

Rating 2 Points

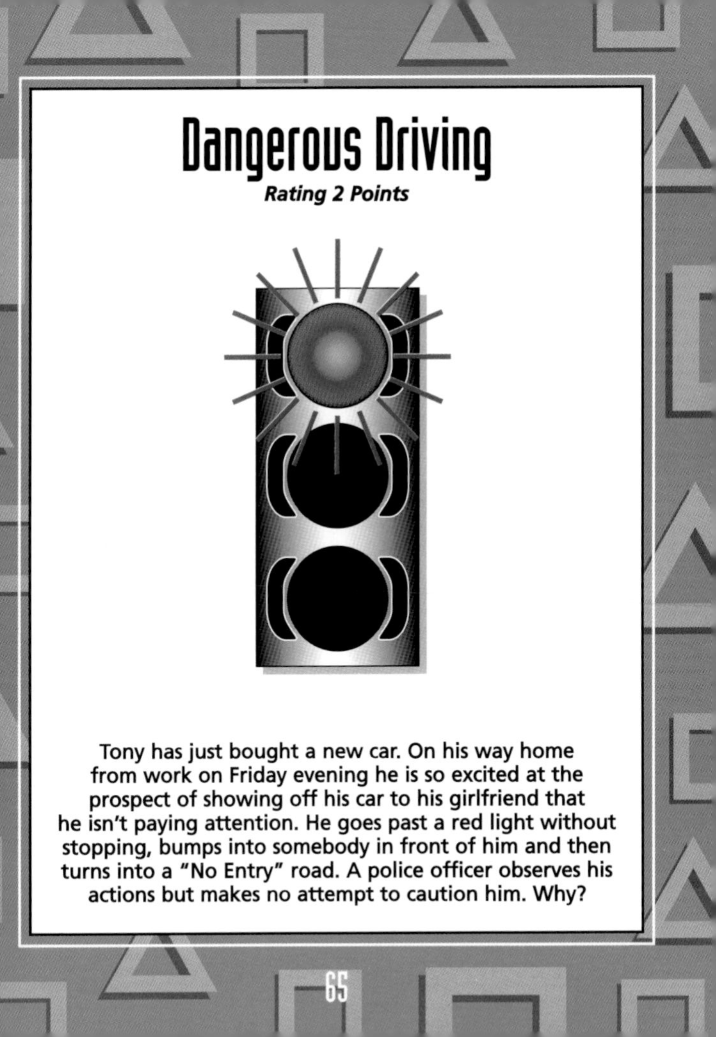

Tony has just bought a new car. On his way home from work on Friday evening he is so excited at the prospect of showing off his car to his girlfriend that he isn't paying attention. He goes past a red light without stopping, bumps into somebody in front of him and then turns into a "No Entry" road. A police officer observes his actions but makes no attempt to caution him. Why?

Dangerous Driving - Solution

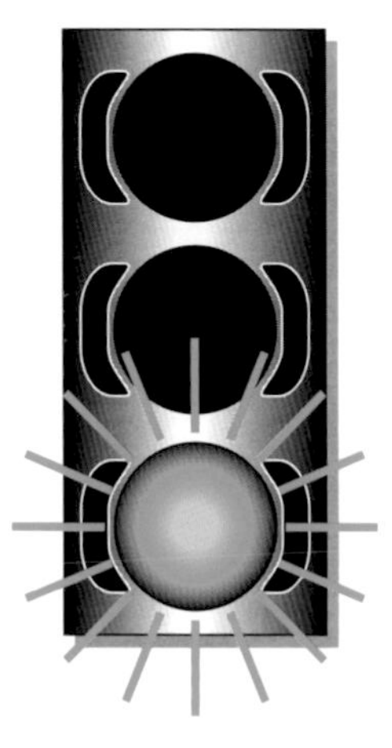

Tony was walking home.
His new car had been delivered to his house.

Lovers' Tiff

Rating 2 Points

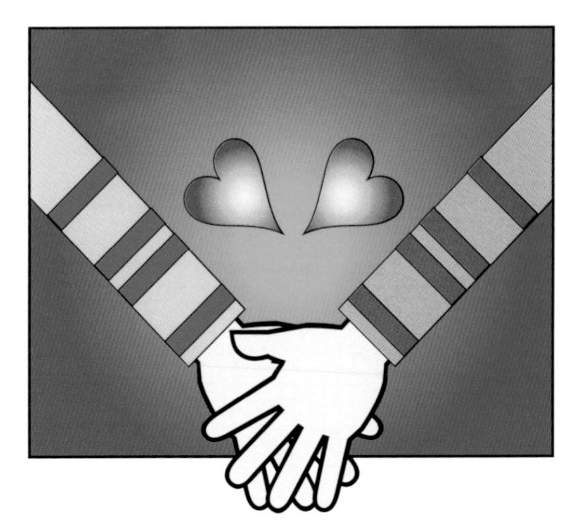

A group of friends are sitting around a table in a pub. Carol asks Dave to hold her hand, then goes up to the bar to order a round of drinks. When she returns, all the others are accusing Dave of being a cheat. Both Dave and Carol are single so why all the fuss?

Lovers' Tiff - Solution

They are playing cards and Dave has looked at Carol's hand.

Family Reunion

Rating 1 Point

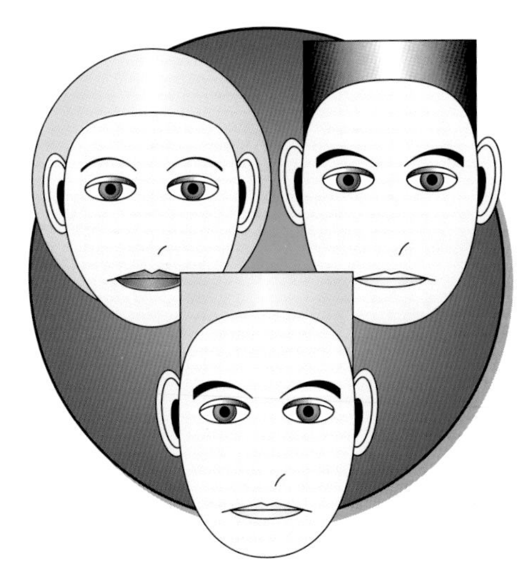

Jim and his wife, Jane, are walking in the park with Bob and his wife, Lyn. Jim and Bob are brothers. They suddenly bump into Lyn's older brother who is playing football with his little boy, Jack. Jane exclaims to the little boy: "What a lovely surprise to see my little nephew!" Explain.

Family Reunion - Solution

The two women are sisters: two brothers have married two sisters.

Room Temperature Test

Rating 1 Point

One tub contains water at 20 degrees Centigrade, another at 20 degrees Fahrenheit. In which tub does George choose to give his dog a bath?

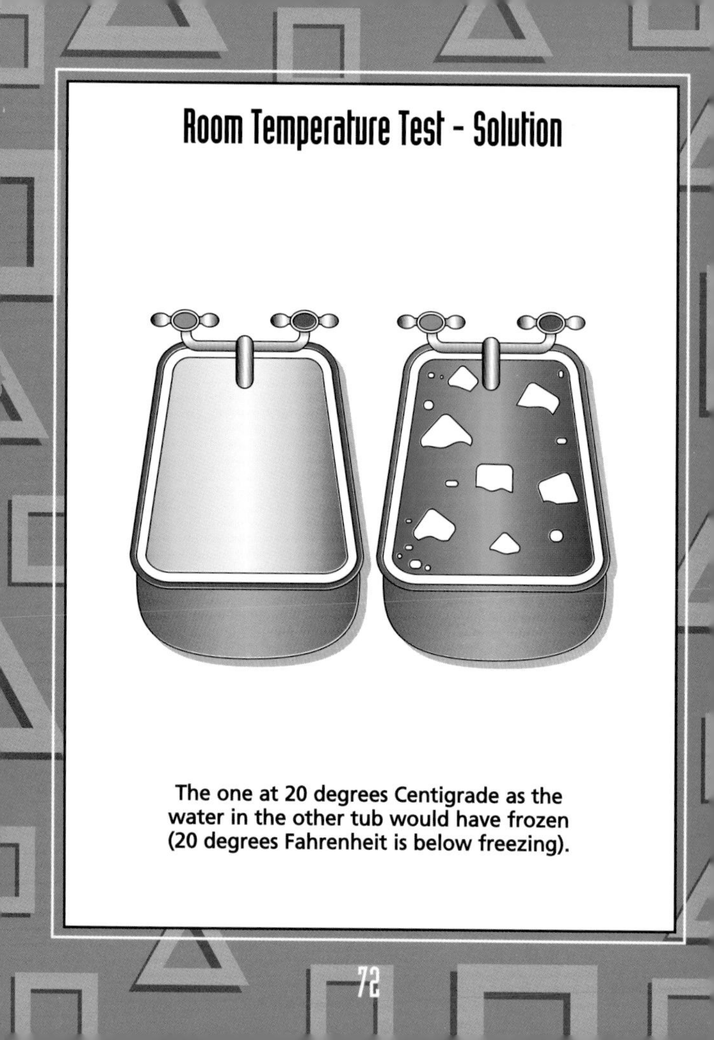

Room Temperature Test - Solution

The one at 20 degrees Centigrade as the water in the other tub would have frozen (20 degrees Fahrenheit is below freezing).

Rising Tide

Rating 2 Points

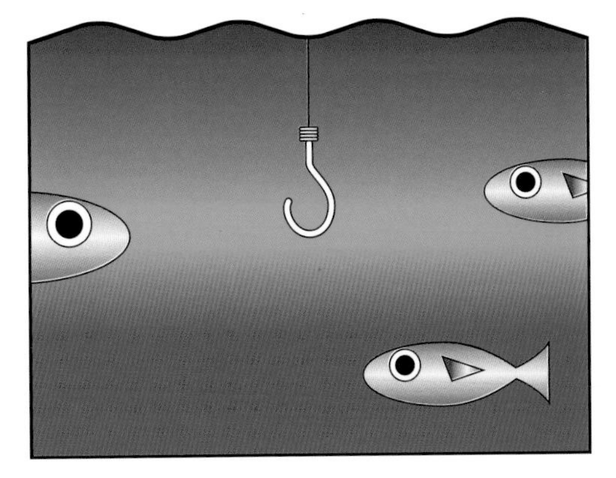

A man is fishing off the side of a barge that is moored against the bank. His fishing hook on the end of his line is 50cm (19.69in) below the surface of the water. If the tide rises 30cm (11.81in) an hour, how far below the water level is the hook after he has been fishing for two hours?

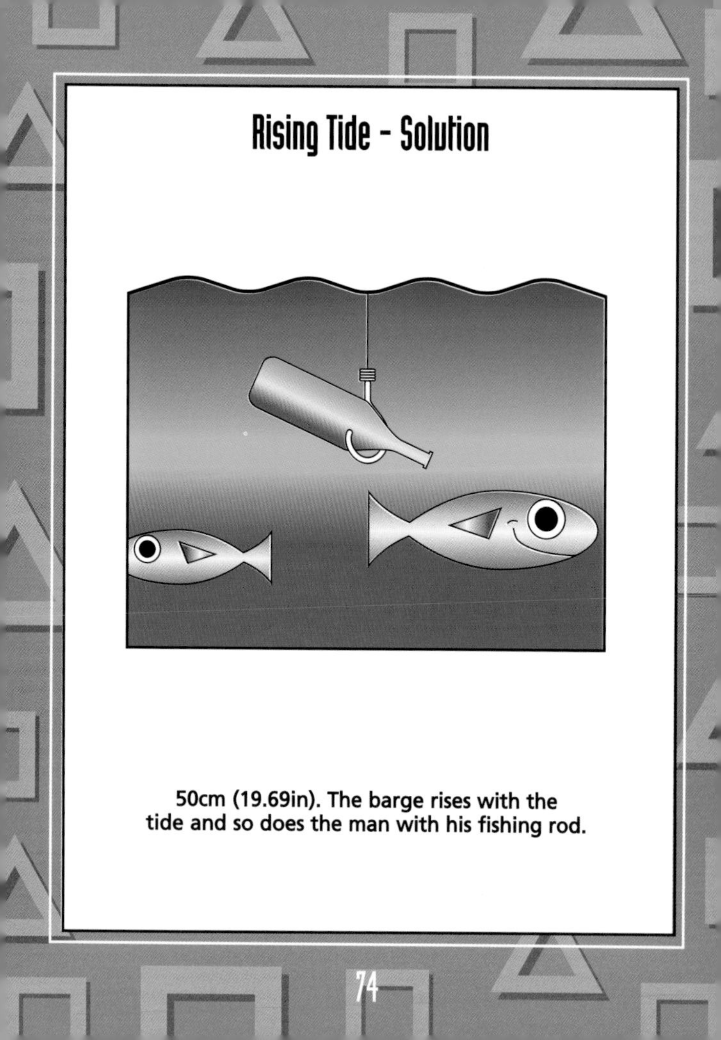

Rising Tide – Solution

50cm (19.69in). The barge rises with the tide and so does the man with his fishing rod.

Rating 1 Point

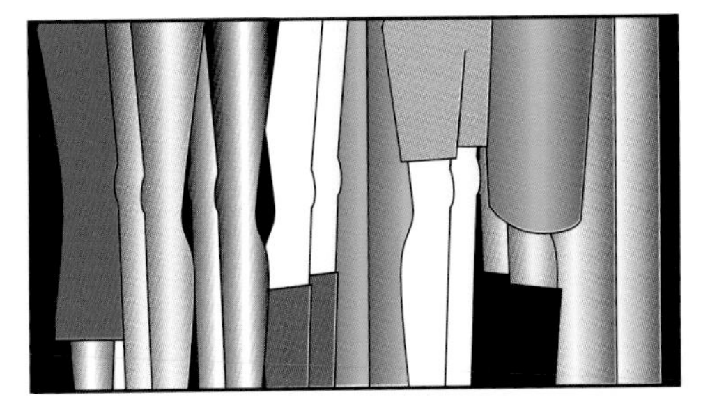

Hiding under a table at his sister's birthday party, Ben can see eight pairs of legs walking around in the living room. After a while, he watches everybody go into an adjoining room to get some food. How is it that there are still six legs in the living room?

Last Legs - Solution

There are Ben's legs plus
the four table legs.

Room with a View

Rating 1 Point

A man lives in a house where all the windows in all of the rooms on each side of the house face in the same direction. Where does he live?

Room with a View - Solution

On the North Pole: all of the windows face south.

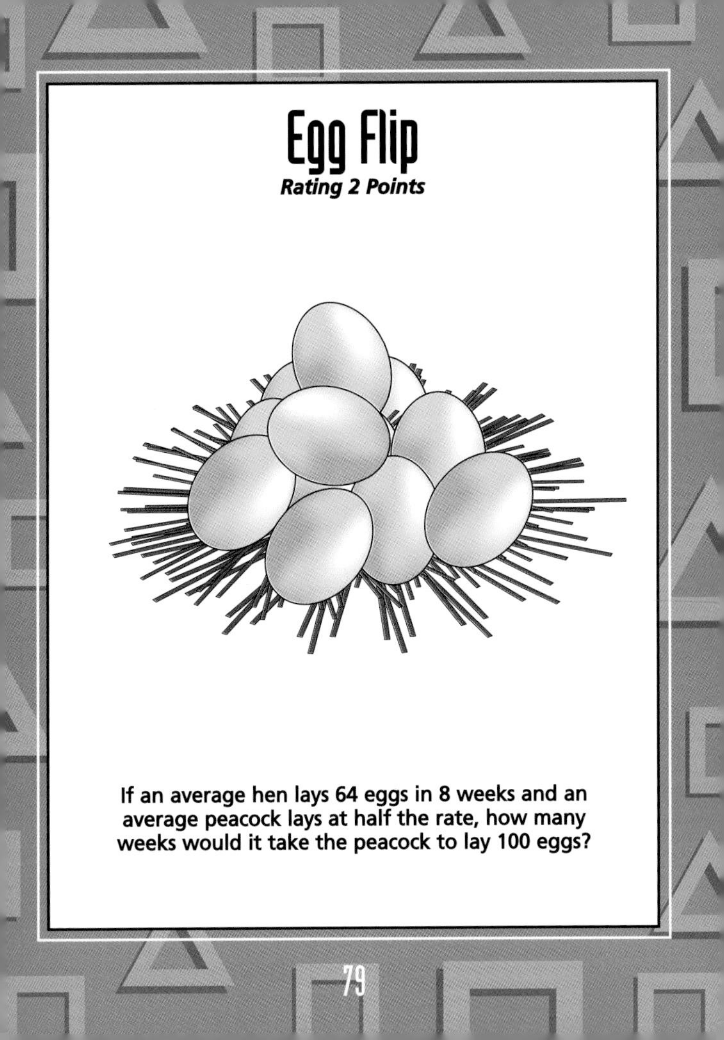

Egg Flip

Rating 2 Points

If an average hen lays 64 eggs in 8 weeks and an average peacock lays at half the rate, how many weeks would it take the peacock to lay 100 eggs?

Egg Flip - Solution

It would take forever because
peahens, not peacocks, lay eggs.

Nightmare Scenario

Rating 3 Points

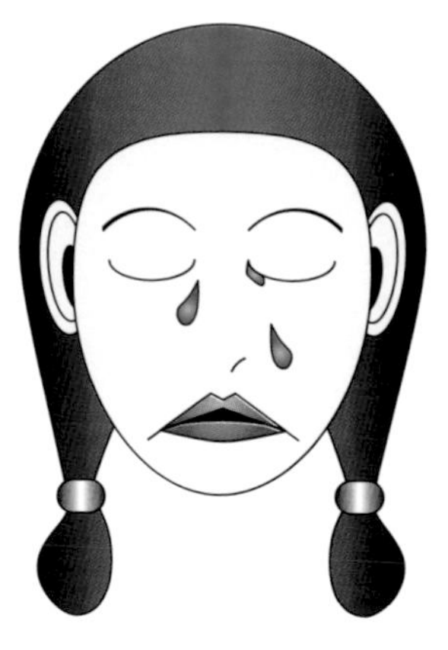

The wife of a dead man was explaining to the doctor that her husband had been watching a programme on the evening of his death about the Beast of Bodmin Moor. Afterwards, she explained, he had had a nightmare in which he was being chased down a hill by a huge black panther-like creature. The husband was tossing about so violently in his sleep, she said, that he rolled off the edge of the bed and died instantly from concussion. Why was the doctor not convinced by the widow's account?

Nightmare Scenario - Solution

The woman could not have known what her husband had been dreaming about since he was not able to tell her before he died.

Sales Slump

Rating 1 Point

In which month are fewest daily newspapers sold?

Sales Slump - Solution

February: there are only
28 (or 29) days in February.

Small Change

Rating 2 Points

Although very old coins tend to be worth more than their face value, why is it that 1980 five cent bits are worth about $100?

Small Change - Solution

1980 refers to the quantity, not the date, so 1980 5 cent pieces equals $99.

Light Work

Rating 3 Points

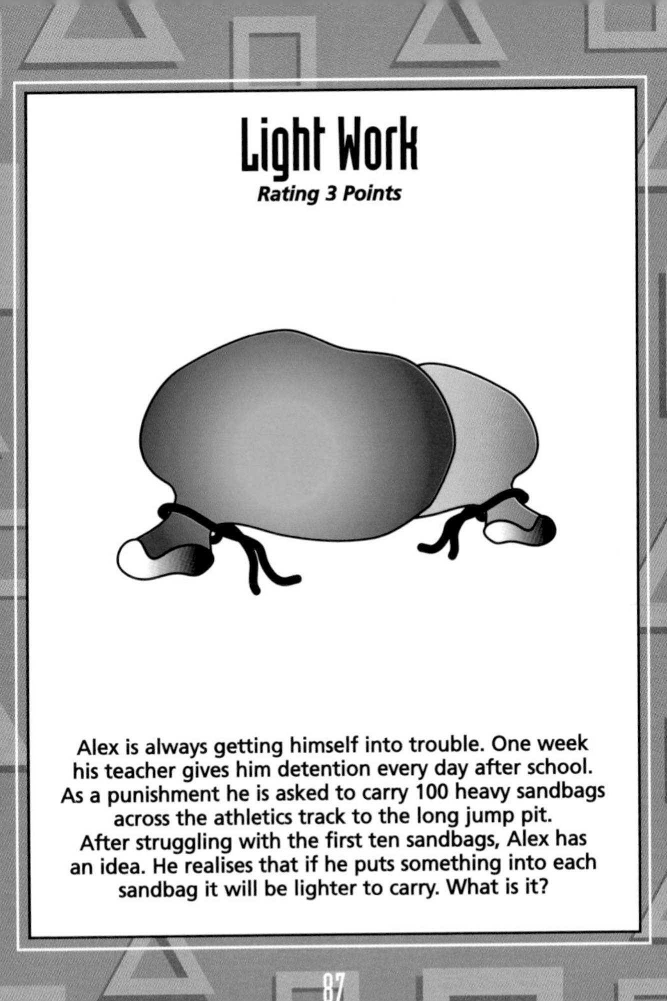

Alex is always getting himself into trouble. One week his teacher gives him detention every day after school. As a punishment he is asked to carry 100 heavy sandbags across the athletics track to the long jump pit. After struggling with the first ten sandbags, Alex has an idea. He realises that if he puts something into each sandbag it will be lighter to carry. What is it?

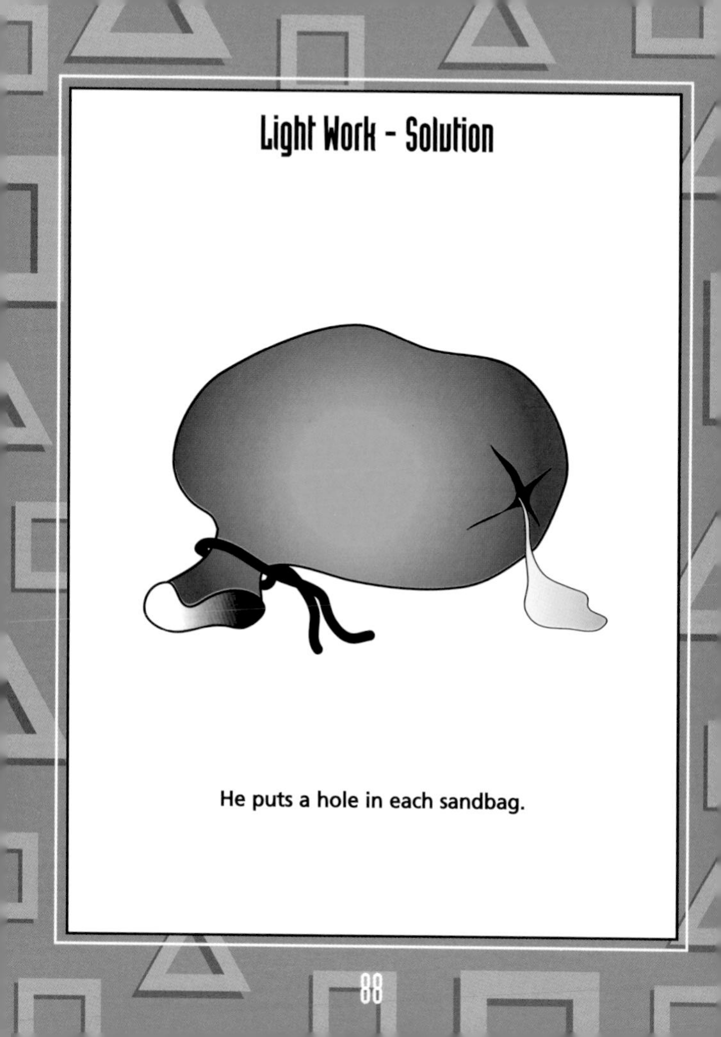

Light Work - Solution

He puts a hole in each sandbag.

Auch Aye the Noo

Rating 2 Points

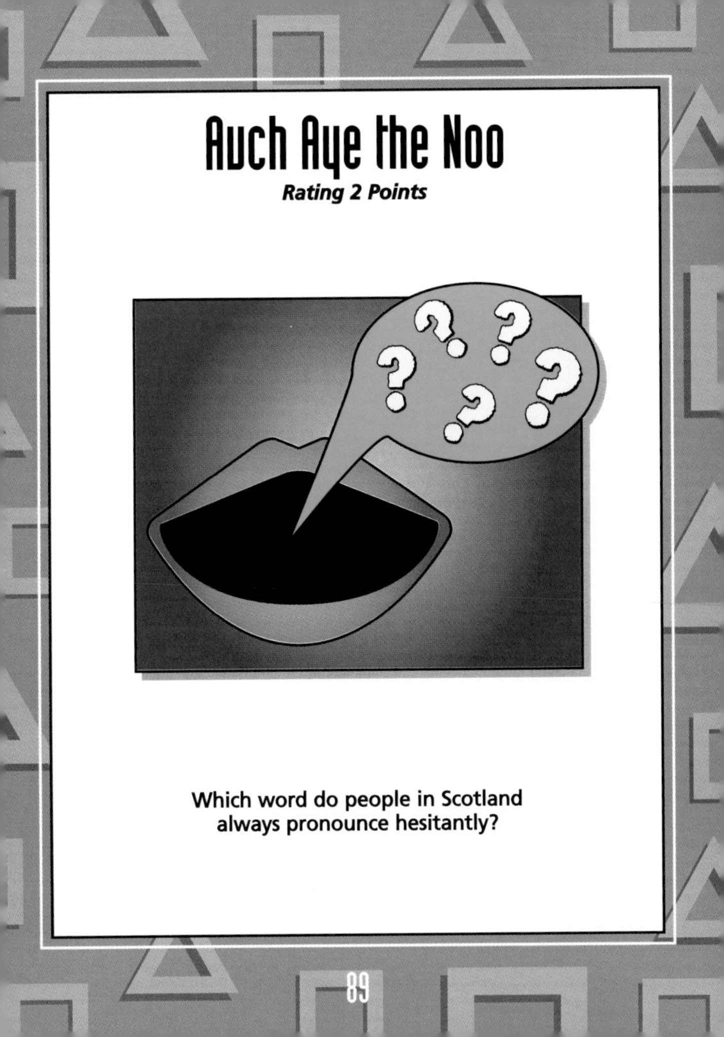

Which word do people in Scotland always pronounce hesitantly?

Auch Aye the Noo - Solution

Hesitantly.

Trivial Pursuits

Rating 1 Point

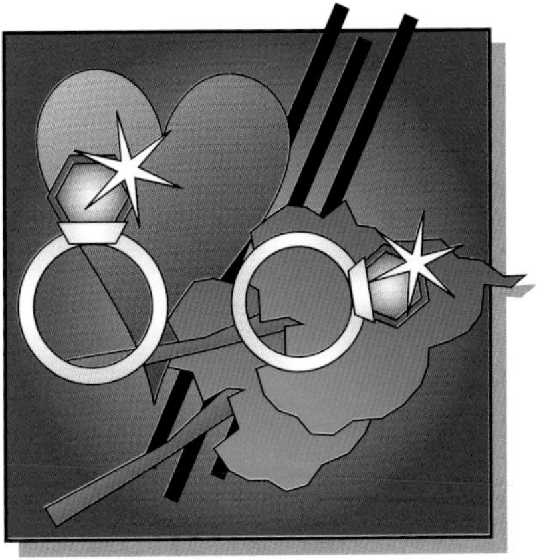

Ian is describing the previous evening to his girlfriend: There were four main groups, each a dozen-strong. Each group included a couple of important people, and there were also one or two comedians in the bunch. They all intermingled very easily, though. You would have enjoyed yourself because we saw lots of precious stones, love hearts and heart-shaped leaves. There were also some black stick-like objects, which we did our best to get rid of. How had Ian spent his evening?

Trivial Pursuits - Solution

Playing cards.

Parent Trouble

Rating 1 Point

Michael says goodbye to his Dad who is about to doze off in the armchair and goes to catch the bus into town. He only has to wait two minutes before the bus pulls up at the bus stop. A little old lady gets on to the bus just before Michael. The bus driver smiles to the little old lady and says happily, "That's my son just behind you!". How can this be?

Parent Trouble - Solution

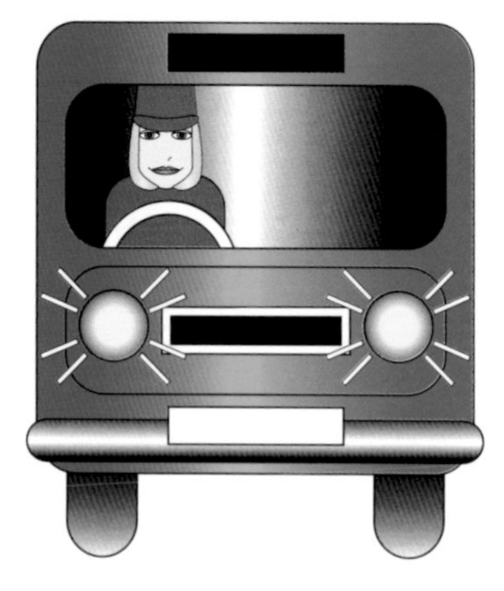

The bus driver is Michael's mum.

Phone Formula

Rating 1 Point

Why do some people dial 911 or 999 with
their index finger and some with their third finger?

Phone Formula - Solution

To call the emergency services.

A Question of Strength

Rating 2 Points

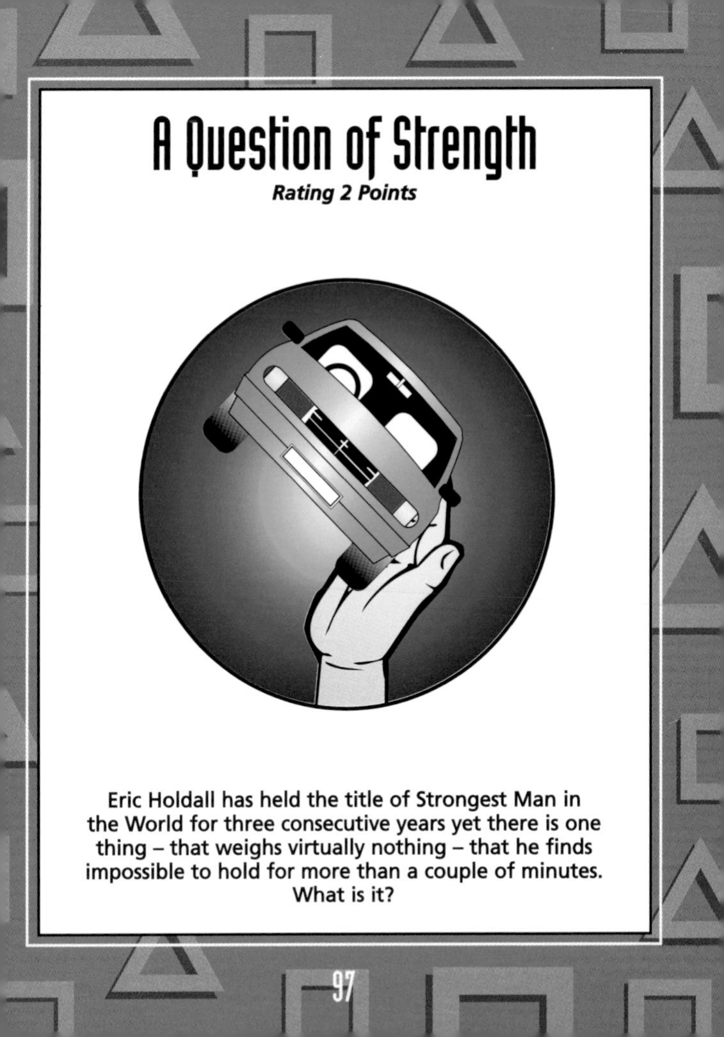

Eric Holdall has held the title of Strongest Man in the World for three consecutive years yet there is one thing – that weighs virtually nothing – that he finds impossible to hold for more than a couple of minutes. What is it?

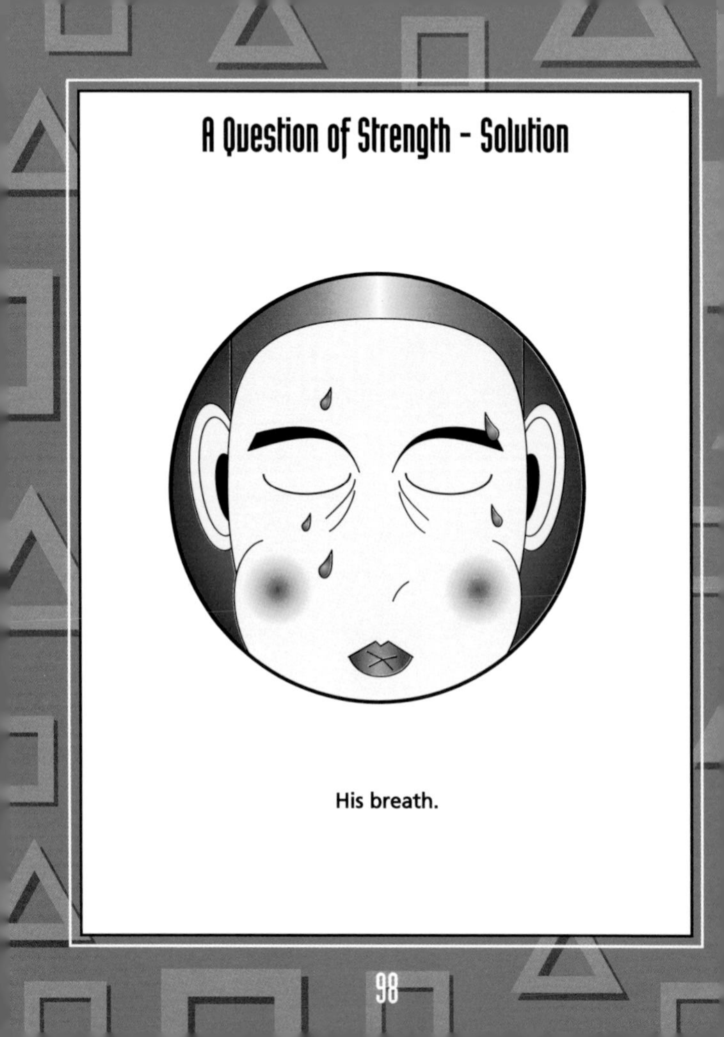

A Question of Strength - Solution

His breath.

Chapter 3

To see individual ratings for each puzzle see under the title of each question.

Once you have completed the chapter, turn to page 100, for help adding up your score.

Then turn to page 145 to start chapter 4.

Chapter 3 - Scoring

Puzzle points for correct answer

Steam Room Stabbing	**2**	Fatal Move	**2**
Triple Tally	**3**	Tattoo Parlour	**1**
Catch Up	**3**	Rash Action	**2**
Polo Knockout	**2**	Rover's Revenge	**2**
Hit and Run	**2**	Discriminating Evidence	**2**
Opera Buff	**1**	Process of Elimination	**2**
Weather Proof	**3**	Camping Catastrophe	**3**
Locked Car Conundrum	**2**	Ancient Inferno	**2**
Avalanche Attack	**1**	Braving the Elements	**1**
Leap Year	**1**	Dangerous Dilemma	**3**
Catch the Boat	**3**	Money Matters	**2**

YOUR TOTAL

45

Steam Room Stabbing

Rating 2 Points

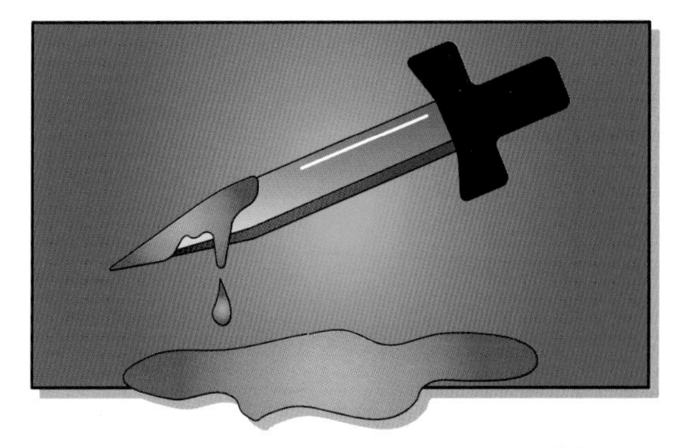

One Wednesday afternoon Blake visits a health spa where he meets three other men, Peter, Paul and Carl. They undress and then enter the steam room. Peter is a musician and has brought his walkman, and Paul and Carl have both brought books to read. Blake has taken a thermos flask. Before long, a piercing cry is heard in the mist-filled room, and one of Blake's companions is found dead from a stab wound to the chest. When the police come to investigate and question the three men, all they find in the room are a walkman, two books and an empty thermos.
No weapon is found and no one else has entered or left the room. What had happened?

Steam Room Stabbing - Solution

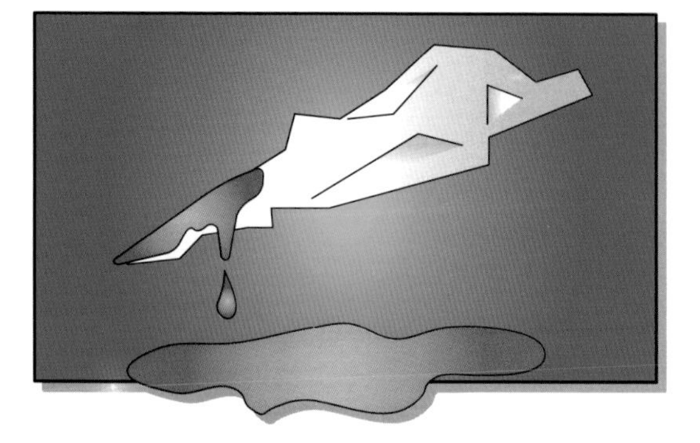

Blake had committed the murder.
His thermos flask contained an ice dagger, which he used to stab the man in the chest. The weapon then melted in the steam before anyone else saw it.

Triple Tally

Rating 3 Points

Three pupils are each asked to select four numbers under ten and multiply them together. They all come up with the same answer, even though they don't all pick the same numbers. How?

Triple Tally - Solution

They all selected 0 as one of their four numbers, so all their answers were 0.

Catch Up

Rating 3 Points

Steve and Sally decided to get away from their hectic life in the city for a quiet weekend in the country. After a long and tiring journey, they arrive at a guesthouse, unpack, wind up their alarm clock and get into bed at 9pm. Steve falls asleep by 9:15 and Sally by 9:30. As they fully intend to catch up on a lot of sleep over the weekend they had both agreed to lie in in the morning and they had set the alarm for 11:30. How much sleep had they both had when the alarm went off?

Catch up - Solution

Steve had slept for 2 hours 15 minutes and Sally for 2 hours – it was a wind up clock not a 24-hour clock so the alarm would have gone off at 11.30pm.

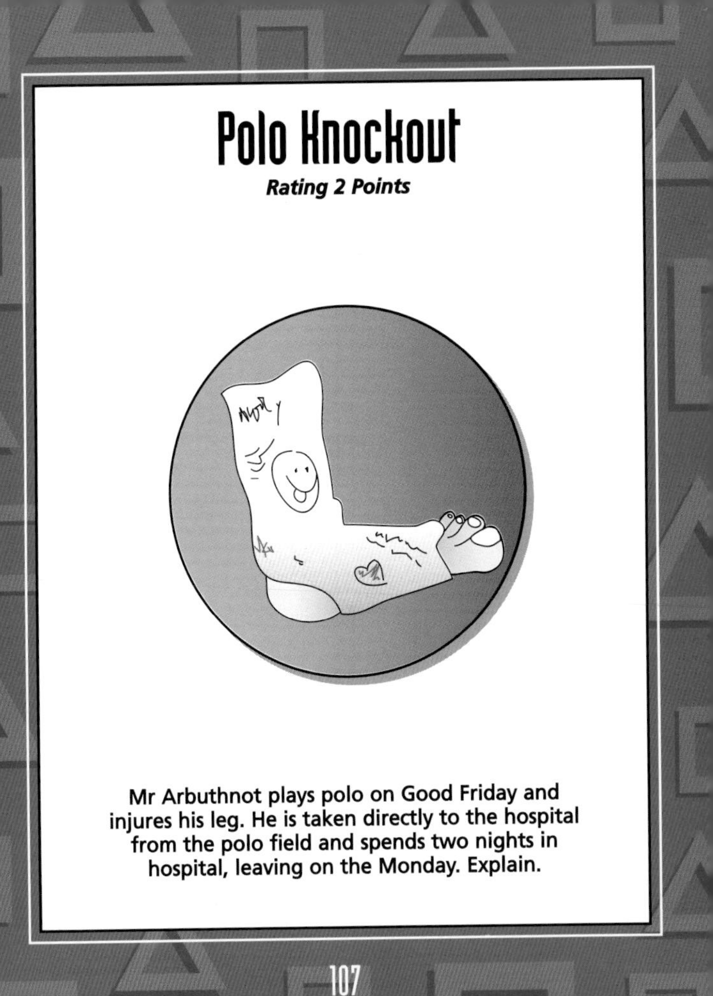

Polo Knockout

Rating 2 Points

Mr Arbuthnot plays polo on Good Friday and injures his leg. He is taken directly to the hospital from the polo field and spends two nights in hospital, leaving on the Monday. Explain.

Polo Knockout - Solution

Mr Arbuthnot's horse is called Good Friday.
He was playing polo on Saturday.

Hit and Run

Rating 2 Points

A man gets into a taxi and names his destination. No more is said between them. The driver takes the man, who he has never met before, to a secluded spot, lures him out of the taxi and kills him. This behaviour is completely uncharacteristic of the usually placid taxi driver. What was his motive?

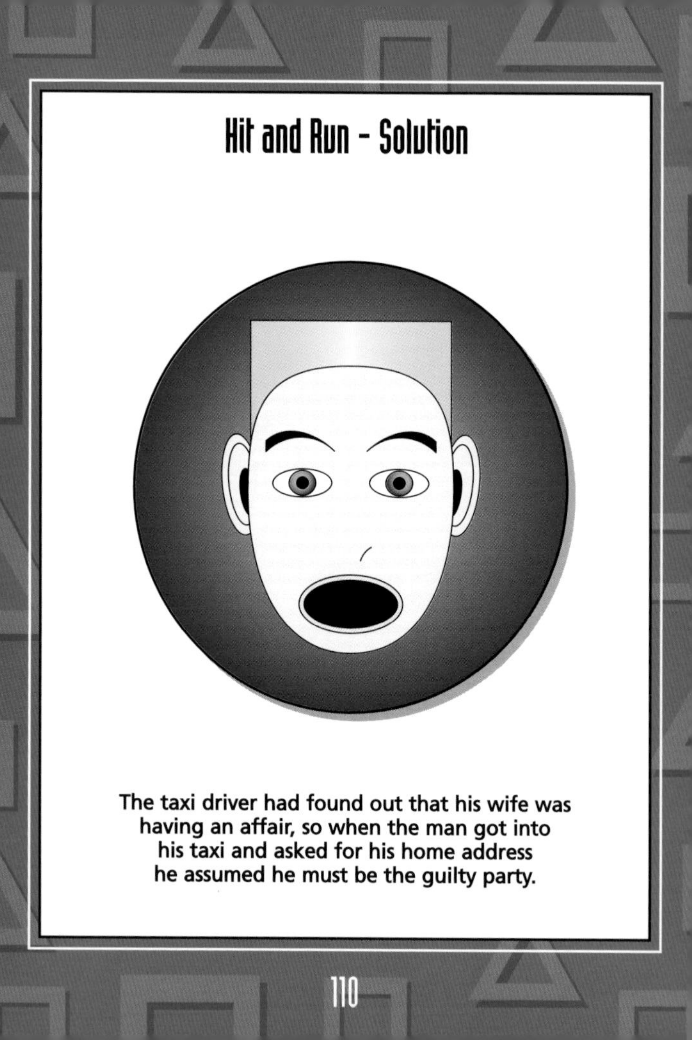

Hit and Run - Solution

The taxi driver had found out that his wife was having an affair, so when the man got into his taxi and asked for his home address he assumed he must be the guilty party.

Opera Buff

Rating 1 Point

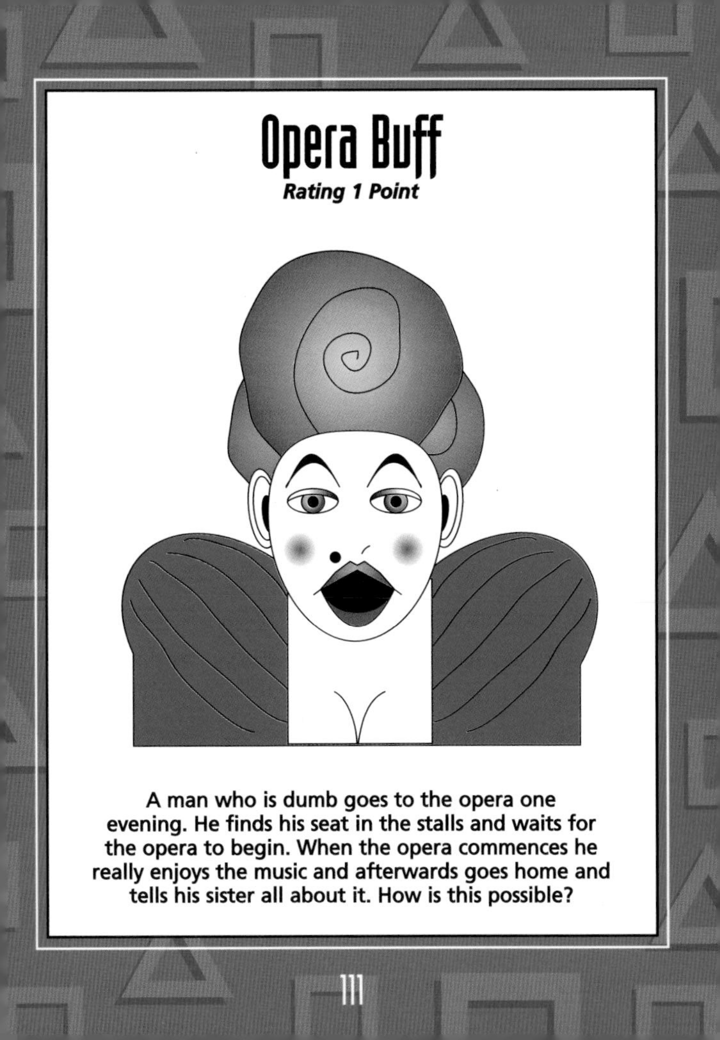

A man who is dumb goes to the opera one evening. He finds his seat in the stalls and waits for the opera to begin. When the opera commences he really enjoys the music and afterwards goes home and tells his sister all about it. How is this possible?

Opera Buff - Solution

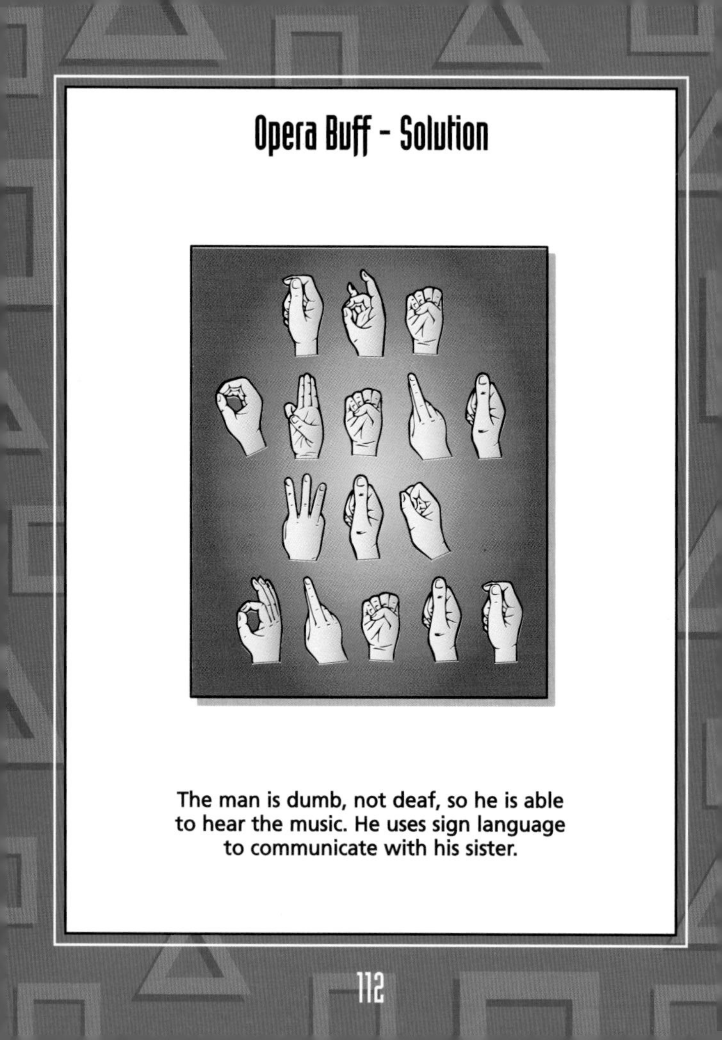

The man is dumb, not deaf, so he is able to hear the music. He uses sign language to communicate with his sister.

Weather Proof

Rating 3 Points

A man is driving slowly through a town. He is carrying two passengers, one in the front and one in the back. On arriving at their destination, where they meet up with four others, they all get out and it begins to rain. Six of them get wet, even though they hurry on their way. The passenger who was in the back of the car, however, remains completely dry, even though he makes no attempt to hurry and has no hat, coat or umbrella. How is this possible?

Weather Proof - Solution

The passenger in the back is in a coffin,
which has been conveyed to the
destination – a church – by hearse.

Locked Car Conundrum

Rating 2 Points

Len parks his car, locks the doors and goes off for a walk in the park. After some time he returns to his car and realises that he has lost his keys while walking in the park. "Damn," he thought, "I'll never find them". Then he smiled, realising he had a spare set of keys in the glove compartment. Seconds later Len is driving home without having forced his way into the car. He didn't break a window or seek any other assistance, so how did he get into the locked car?

Locked Car Conundrum - Solution

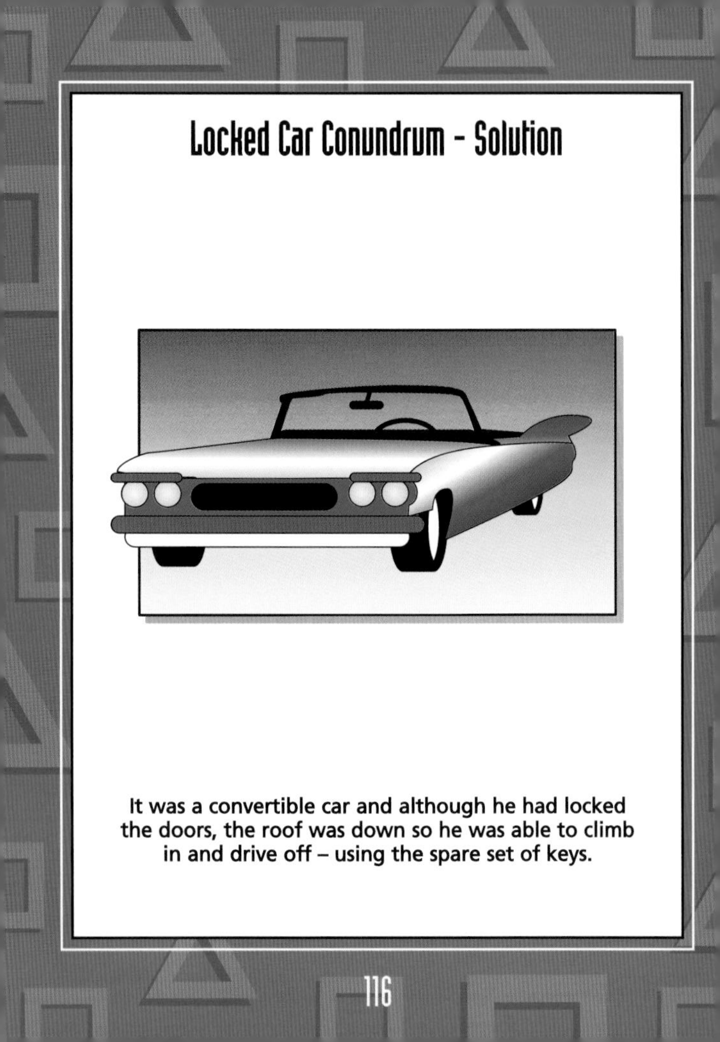

It was a convertible car and although he had locked the doors, the roof was down so he was able to climb in and drive off – using the spare set of keys.

Avalanche Attack

Rating 1 Point

On holiday in the Pyrennees, Stuart and Matt are skiing down the mountainside when suddenly an avalanche strikes. Stuart is nearly saved, but Matt is nearly buried under the snow. Who is the more grateful?

Avalanche Attack - Solution

Matt: he survives, whereas Stuart, who is nearly saved, is in fact trapped under the snow.

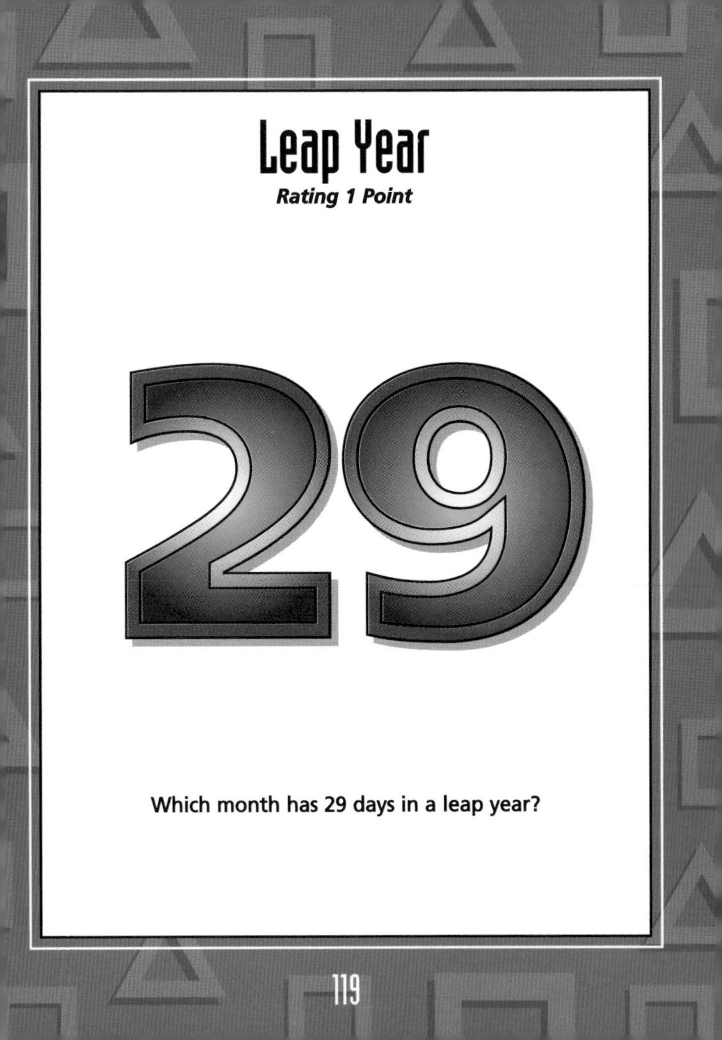

Leap Year

Rating 1 Point

Which month has 29 days in a leap year?

Leap Year - Solution

JANUARY
FEBRUARY
MARCH
APRIL
MAY
JUNE
JULY
AUGUST
SEPTEMBER
OCTOBER
NOVEMBER
DECEMBER

Every month.

Catch the Boat

Rating 3 Points

A tourist, thinking he is late, rushes from his hotel and runs to the quayside where he sees his ferry at some distance from the docks. He pushes his way through the crowds, and precariously leaps onto the ferry with his suitcase. Miraculously he is unharmed; he sighs with relief and begins to make himself comfortable on the ferry. A moment later he glances back at the quayside and his heart sinks. Why?

Catch the Boat - Solution

He realises the ferry is about to dock.
It hadn't just left port as he had surmised.

Fatal Move

Rating 2 Points

A man took a chance and moved his car from Pall Mall to a hotel on the Strand. He soon realised the move would bankrupt him. How?

Fatal Move – Solution

He was playing Monopoly and realised he didn't have enough money to pay the rent.

Tattoo Parlour

Rating 1 Point

Ivor wants a tattoo on his arm. There are only two tattooists in the small village where he lives, and Ivor visits both before deciding where to have his done. The first one shows him a recent tattoo of a bird on his shoulder – Ivor is not very impressed, either by the tattoo or by the state of the room, so he goes to the second tattooist in the village. This one has a recent tattoo on his back which he is proud to show to Ivor. Ivor is very impressed by what he sees and decides he would like one just the same. Why then does Ivor decide to return to the first tattooist in order to have the work done?

Tattoo Parlour - Solution

As there are only two tattooists in the village, Ivor assumes that they do work on each other. As he likes the second tattoo he sees, he realises it must have been done by the first tattooist.

Rash Action

Rating 2 Points

A man has a blazing argument with his wife one morning. He goes out and throws himself headlong off a sheer rockface. Later in the evening he returns home unharmed. Explain.

Rash Action - Solution

The man has done a bungee jump.

Rover's Revenge
Rating 2 Points
Rover, a naughty dog, is muzzled and tied to a lead 3m (9.84ft) in length. He spots a ball to play with 10m (32.8ft) away on the other side of the yard. How does Rover succeed in reaching the ball without it rolling towards him?

Rover's Revenge - Solution

He can run across the yard because the other end of his lead is not attached to anything.

Discriminating Evidence

Rating 2 Points

On his way into work one morning, homicide cop Harry Schultz caught sight of excon Frank Delgordo disappearing through the back door of the precinct. Despite knowing full well that Delgordo had entered the station in the early hours of the morning and had spent at least two hours destroying finger prints, he made no move to arrest him. Why?

Discriminating Evidence - Solution

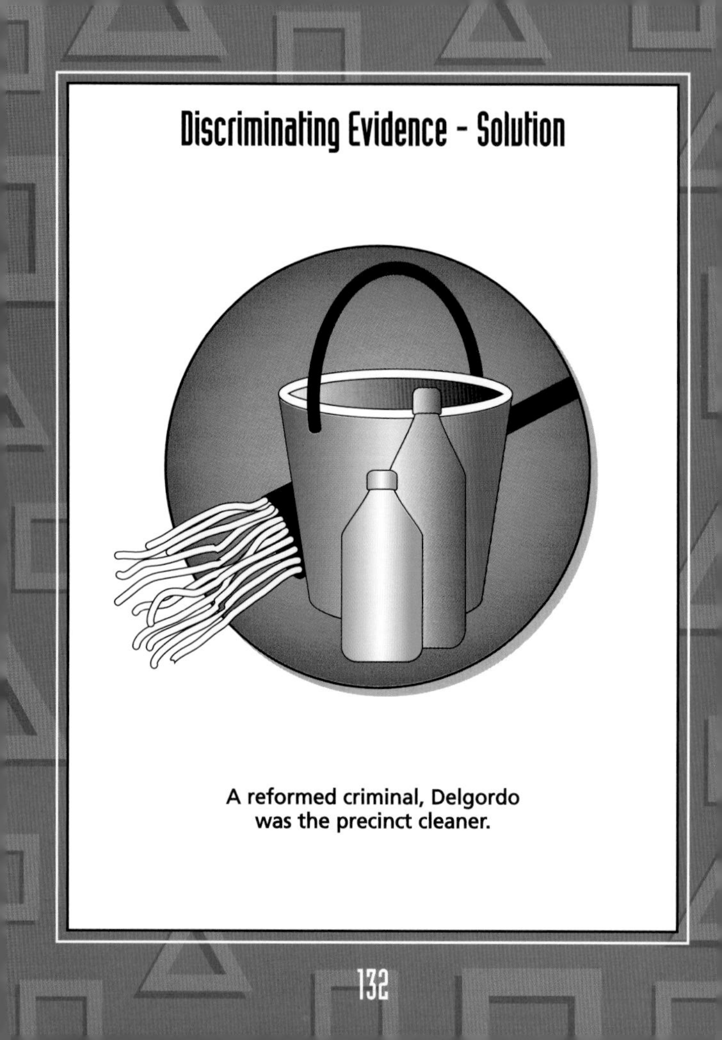

A reformed criminal, Delgordo was the precinct cleaner.

Process of Elimination

Rating 2 Points

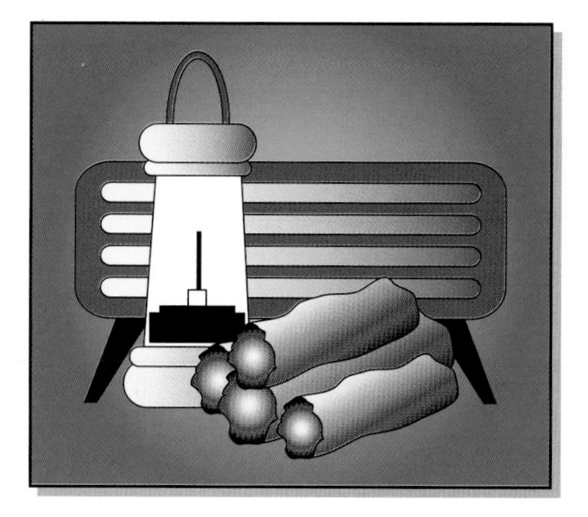

On the last night of a Polar expedition, four intrepid travellers are down to their very last match. They have to make an important decision: they have an oil lamp, a small gas fire and a stove full of wood. Which should they light first if they are to survive the freezing night air?

Process of Elimination – Solution

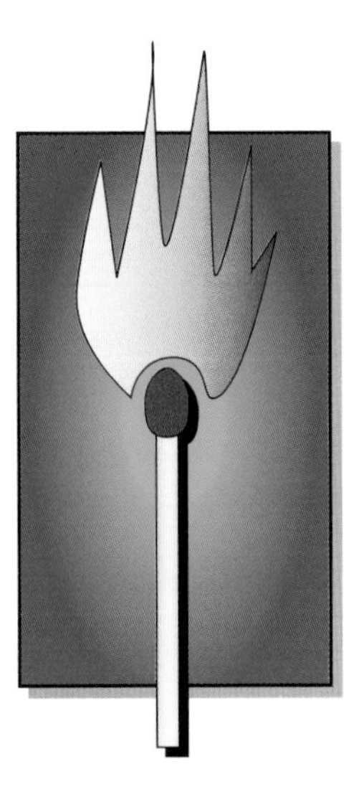

The match.

Camping Catastrophe

Rating 3 Points

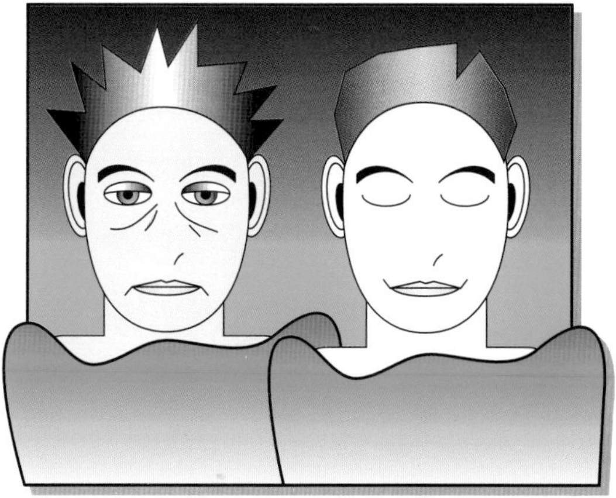

Derek and Mark go camping for the weekend. It is 10pm once they have finished pitching their tent. Derek gets into his sleeping bag and falls straight asleep, but Mark tosses and turns, unable to get to sleep even though he is extremely tired. At midnight, a noisy animal passing the tent wakes Derek up, and Mark promptly falls asleep. Why is this?

Camping Catastrophe - Solution

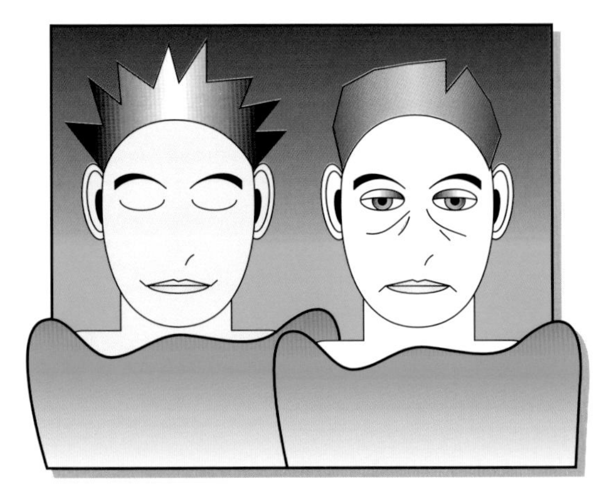

Mark couldn't sleep because Derek was snoring. When Derek awoke he stopped snoring which enabled Mark to drop off to sleep.

Ancient Inferno

Rating 2 Points

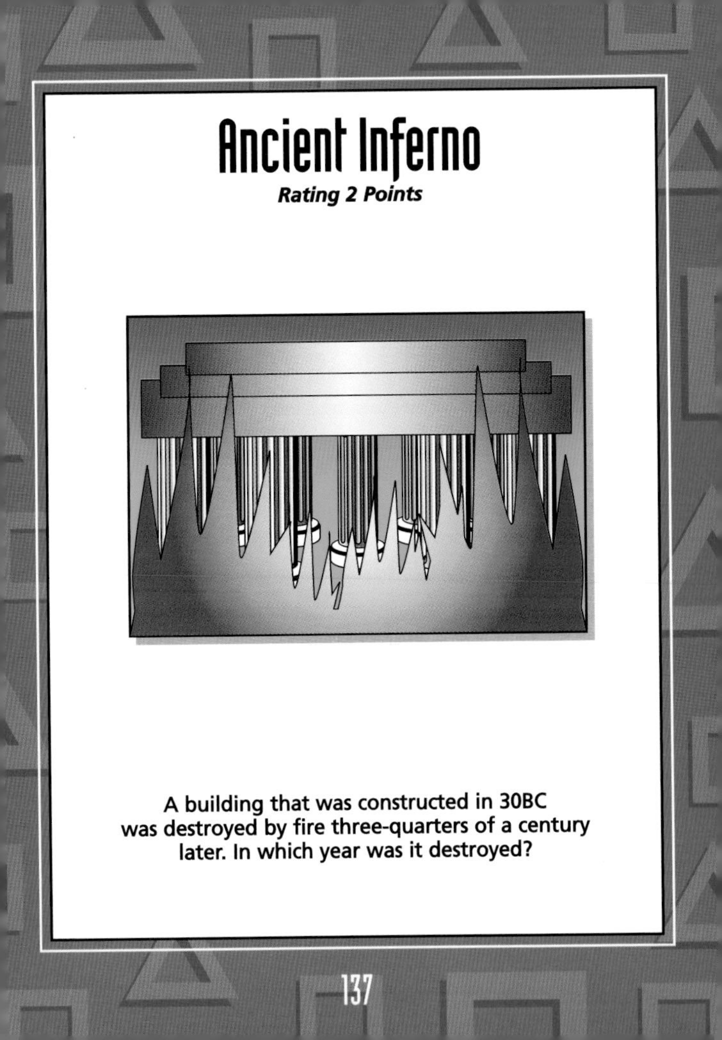

A building that was constructed in 30BC
was destroyed by fire three-quarters of a century
later. In which year was it destroyed?

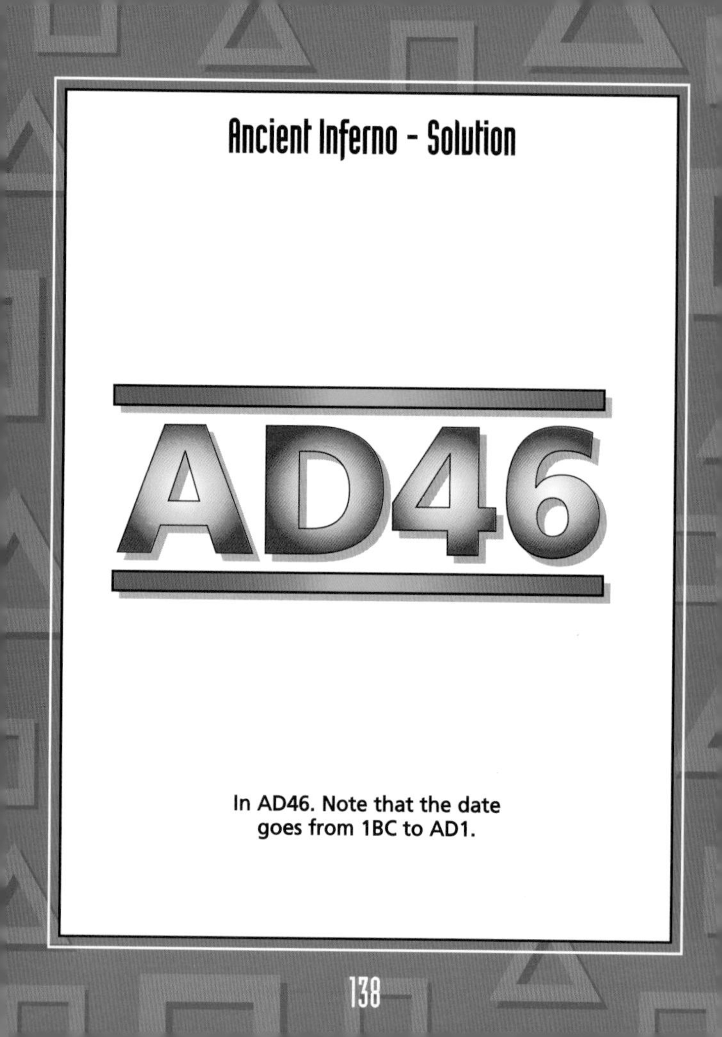

Ancient Inferno - Solution

In AD46. Note that the date
goes from 1BC to AD1.

Braving the Elements

Rating 1 Point

The west coast of Scotland is renowned for being very rainy. All the locals wear raincoats but holidaymaker Mick has no coat, hat or umbrella. He sits in a café drinking a steaming mug of hot coffee. He reads a newspaper to pass the time but eventually decides he should be on his way. To get back to his hotel he needs to walk across a large field and through a treeless park, yet he arrives back at his hotel bone dry. How has he avoided getting wet?

Braving the Elements - Solution

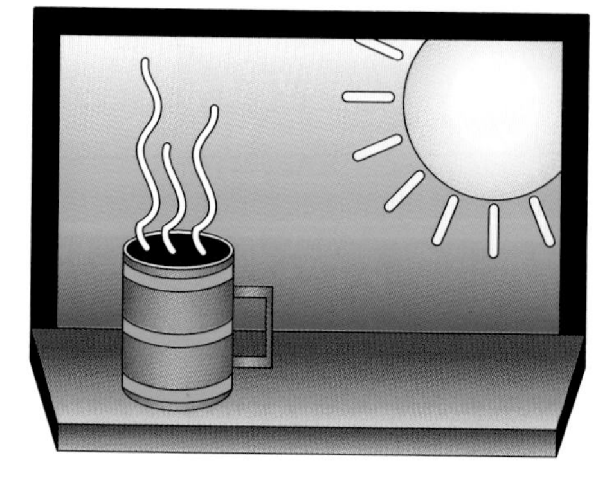

It wasn't raining.

Dangerous Dilemma

Rating 3 Points

A boy is captured by a cruel master who tells him he will have to become a servant to one of his two sons, Theo the Terrible or Angus the Awful. The boy is determined to escape such a punishment. The master gives the boy one chance to make a single statement that will decide his future. If what he says is true he is to serve Theo the Terrible, but if what he says is false he is to serve Angus the Awful. What does the boy say to earn his freedom?

Dangerous Dilemma – Solution

I will serve Angus the Awful. If the master were to make the boy serve Angus the Awful his statement will have been true, in which case he should have made him servant to Theo the Terrible, but if he were made to serve Theo the Terrible then his statement will have been false. The master cannot win, so he releases the boy.

Money Matters

Rating 2 Points

What is the difference between a crisp new $10 bill and a dirty old torn one?

Money Matters - Solution

$9. The difference between a $10 dollar and a $1 bill.

Chapter 4

To see individual ratings for each puzzle see under the title of each question.

Once you have completed the chapter, turn to page 146, for help adding up your score.

Then turn to page 191 to see your overall score.

Chapter 4 - Scoring

Puzzle points for correct answer

Puzzle	Points	Puzzle	Points
Lost Cause	2	Silent Meeting	3
Call to Order	2	Winning Team	1
Swiss Connection	1	Irish Outrage	2
Fire Fighter	3	Hold Up	2
Conflicting Allegiance	2	Marathon Math	1
Family Outing	3	Speed Racing	2
Identical Twins	3	Forbidden Entry	3
Foregone Conclusion	2	Broken Journey	2
Suspicious Circumstances	1	Chance Meeting	3
Wet Weather	1	Art Form	2
Time Twins	2	Chocolate Temptation	2

YOUR TOTAL

45

Lost Cause

Rating 2 Points

Two men get lost while walking in the woods. One starts walking northwards, whilst the other heads south. They bump into each other a quarter of an hour later. Explain.

Lost Cause – Solution

The two men had not gone for a walk together, but had got lost separately and were within half an hour's walk from each other.

Call to Order

Rating 2 Points

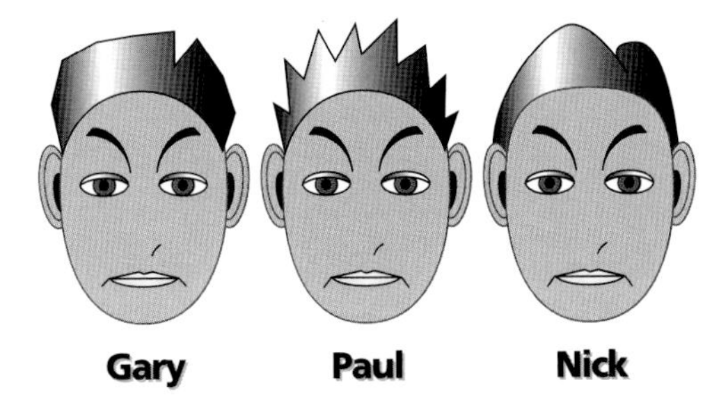

A father asks his three sons, Gary, Nick and Paul, to repeat three times that they are sorry for upsetting their mother. They apologise in unison:

Gary: We are sorry. We are sorry. We are sorry.
Paul: We are sorry. We are sorry.
Nick: We are sorry. We are sorry.
We are sorry. We are sorry.

Which boy did exactly as his father had asked?

Call to Order - Solution

Nick

Nick: he said, We are sorry, and repeated it three times.

Swiss Connection

Rating 1 Point

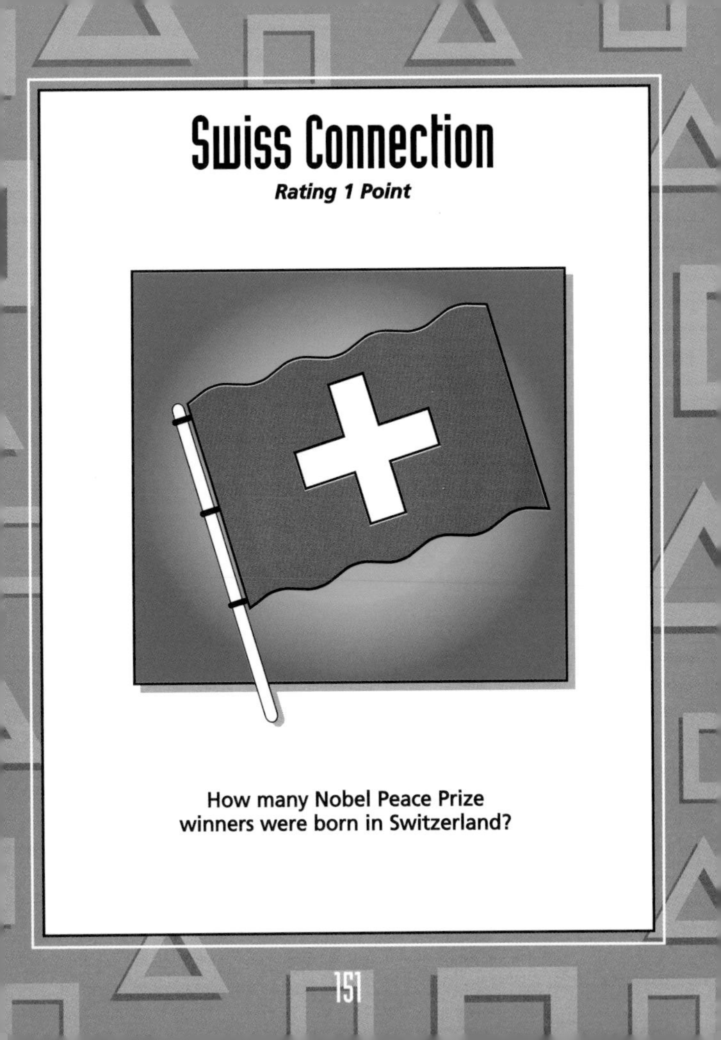

How many Nobel Peace Prize winners were born in Switzerland?

Swiss Connection - Solution

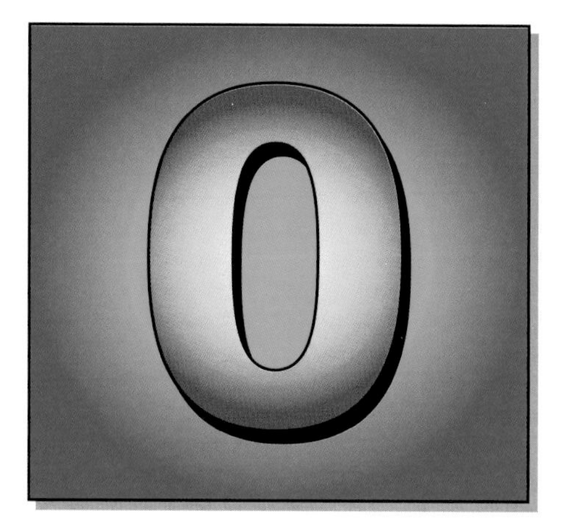

Nobody is born a Nobel
Peace Prize winner.

Fire Fighter

Rating 3 Points

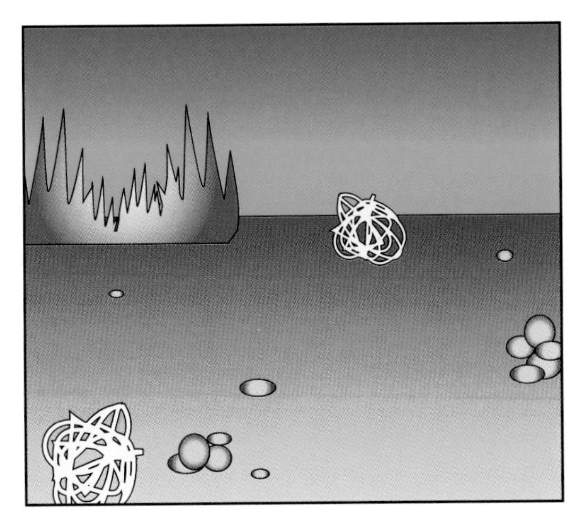

A man is alone on a sunbaked prairie in southern Canada when a fire breaks out and begins spreading rapidly in his direction, aided by the strong westerly wind. He has no means of transport to escape and no water to try and put the fire out. How does the man save himself from the ravages of the fire by making use of a box of matches in his pocket?

Fire Fighter - Solution

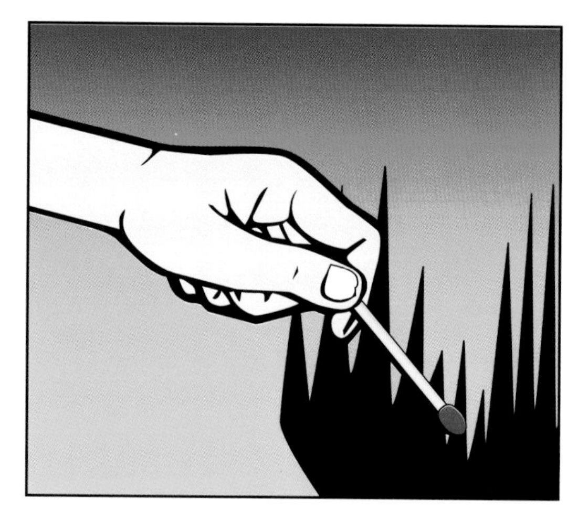

He lights a fire on the ground where he is standing, then he starts walking easterly towards the main fire. The wind will fan his fire further westwards, thus burning out the western end of the prairie. Then he can walk back and wait on a burnt area of land when the main fire approaches.

Conflicting Allegiance

Rating 2 Points

Who played for both Italy and Russia at the Olympic Games in the same year?

Conflicting Allegiance - Solution

The musicians, playing the national anthems for both countries.

Family Outing

Rating 3 Points

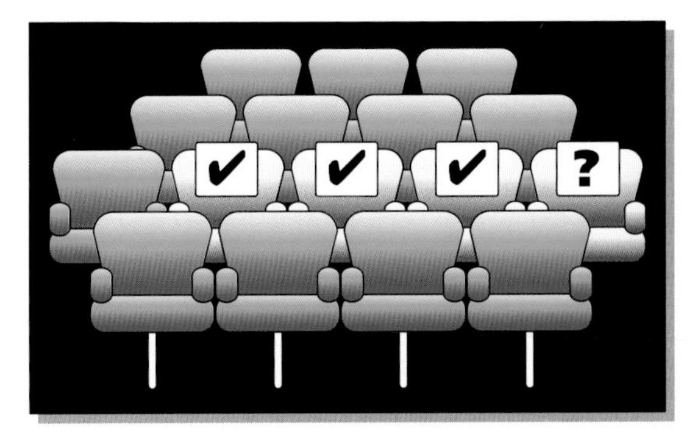

Two sons and two fathers plan to go and see the new blockbuster film at their local cinema. They all see the same 8pm showing together and each has a seat in the front row, yet they had only reserved three tickets. Explain.

Family Outing - Solution

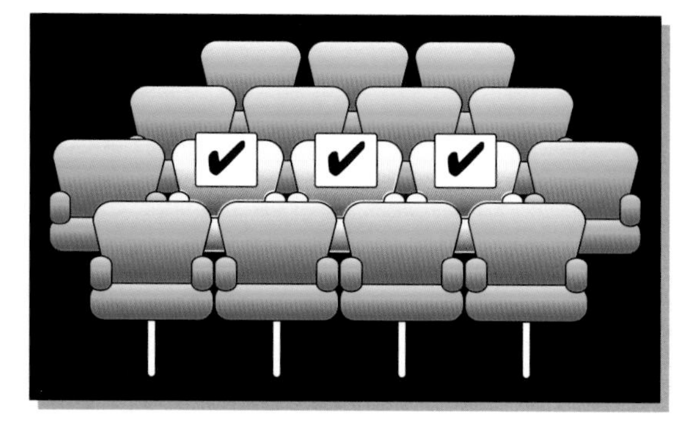

Only three men went to the cinema:
a son, a father and a grandfather.

Identical Twins

Rating 3 Points

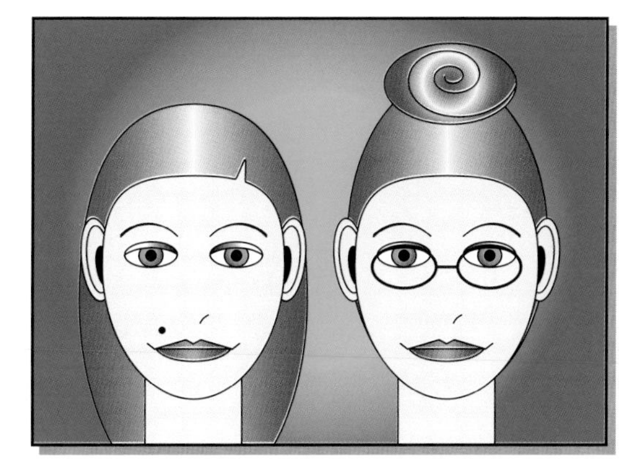

Mr and Mrs Smith have twin daughters: June was born in March and her twin sister, May, was born in June. How can this be?

Identical Twins - Solution

Both were born in the month of
June in the town of March.

Foregone Conclusion

Rating 2 Points

On her first day at the adult education centre, a receptionist has to deliver an urgent message to Pete Smith in the car mechanics course – his wife has suddenly gone into labour. The receptionist rushes into the classroom of some twenty people. How does she instantly know who to give the message to, even though she has never met the man before?

Foregone Conclusion - Solution

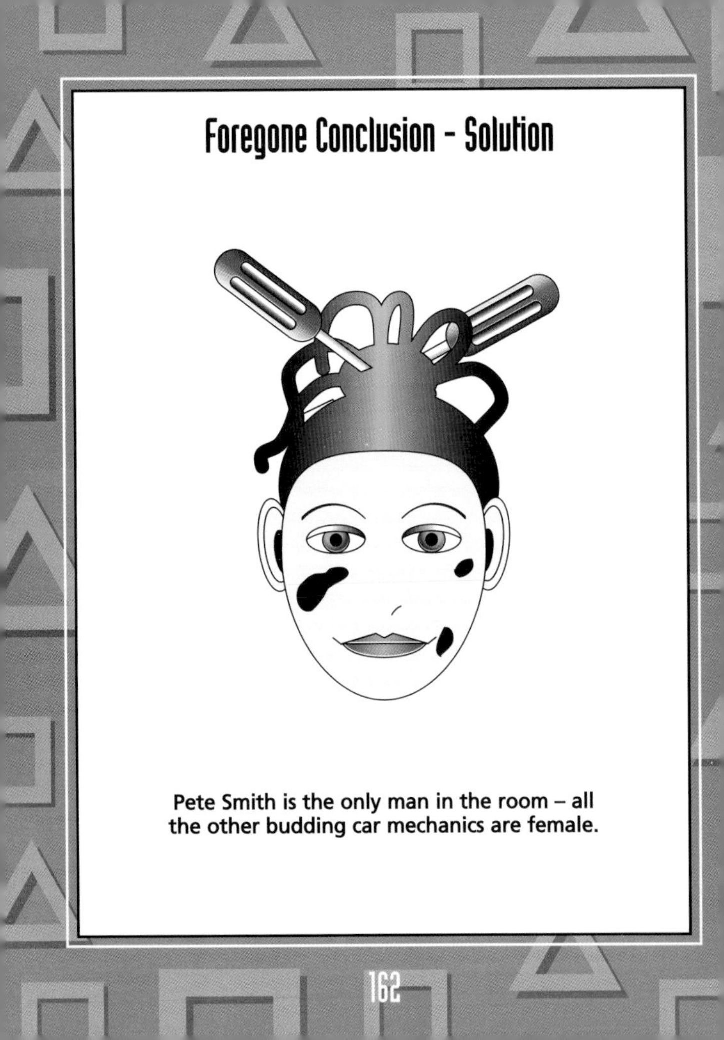

Pete Smith is the only man in the room – all the other budding car mechanics are female.

Suspicious Circumstances

Rating 1 Point

A man lived all by himself. He never went out and no one ever visited him. One day he watered all his plants, turned off all the lights and left the building, never to return again. His action resulted in the death of six men. Why?

Suspicious Circumstances – Solution

The man was a lighthouse keeper. By turning off all the lights he had turned off the beacon light at the top of the lighthouse. Unable to see the rocky shore, a ship had run aground and six sailors had drowned.

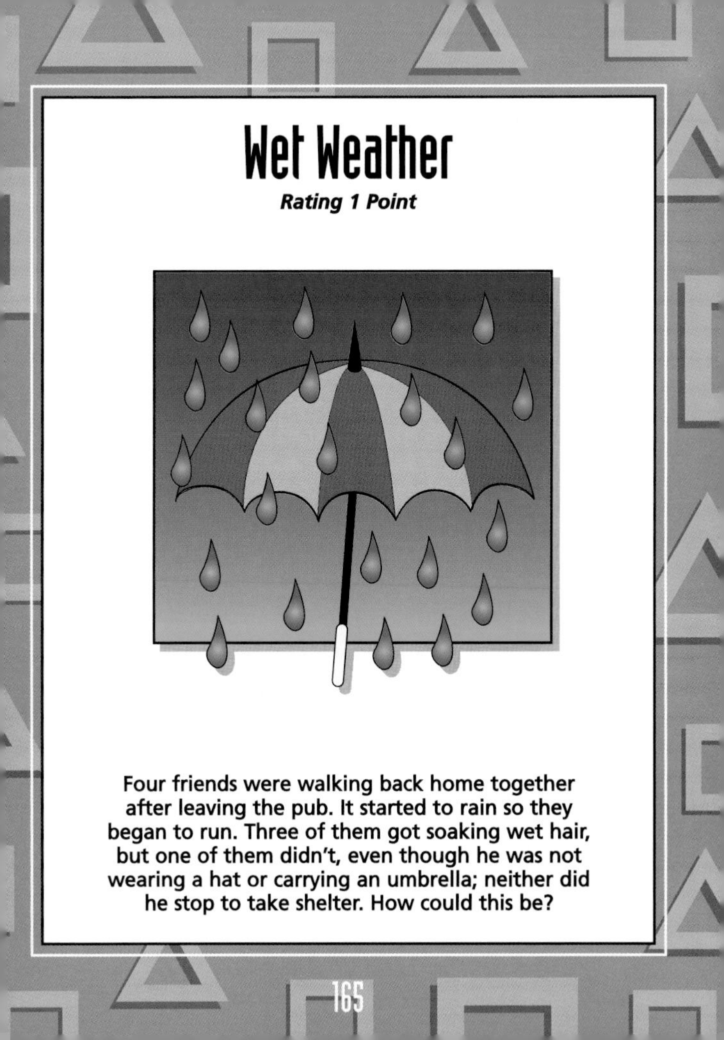

Wet Weather

Rating 1 Point

Four friends were walking back home together after leaving the pub. It started to rain so they began to run. Three of them got soaking wet hair, but one of them didn't, even though he was not wearing a hat or carrying an umbrella; neither did he stop to take shelter. How could this be?

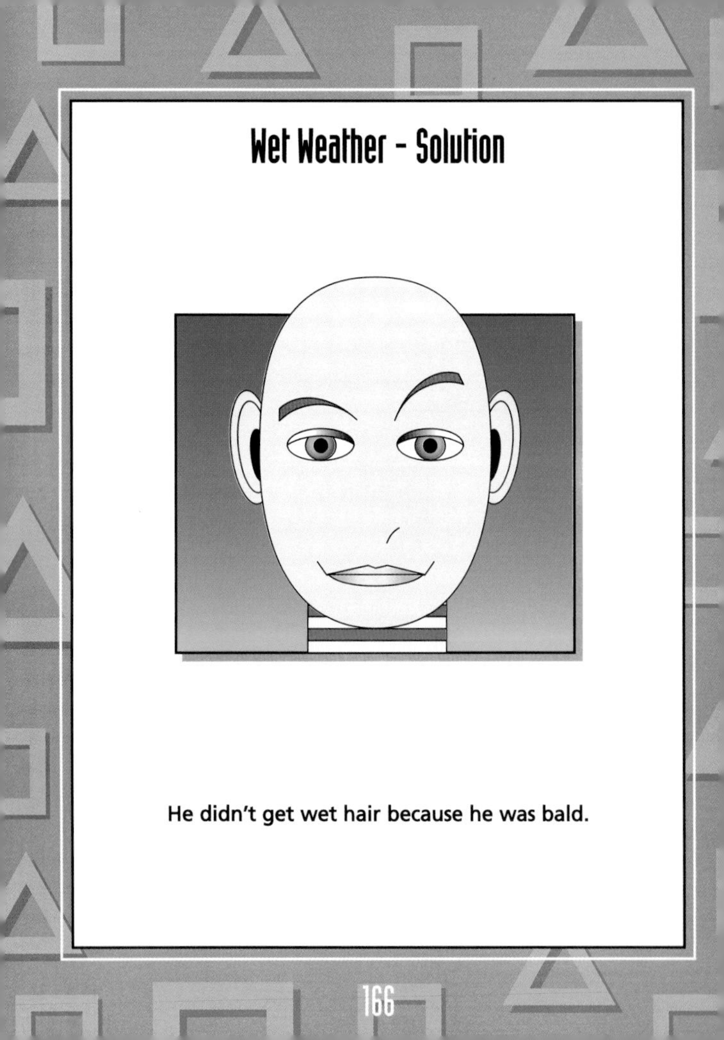

Wet Weather – Solution

He didn't get wet hair because he was bald.

Time Twins

Rating 2 Points

Two brothers have new-born babies exactly 10 hours old. One baby was born in the evening, the other at midday. How can this be?

Time Twins - Solution

One brother lives in Singapore and his baby was born at 8pm. The other baby was born at midday on a winter's day in England, which is 8 hours behind.

Silent Meeting

Rating 3 Points

Kate and Sarah were old friends who had not seen each other for years. One day they met up by chance. Although they spent an hour in each other's company, they did not speak to one another. Neither was deaf or mute and they were still on good terms. Why did they not speak to each other?

Silent Meeting – Solution

They were divers. They were reunited while scuba diving.

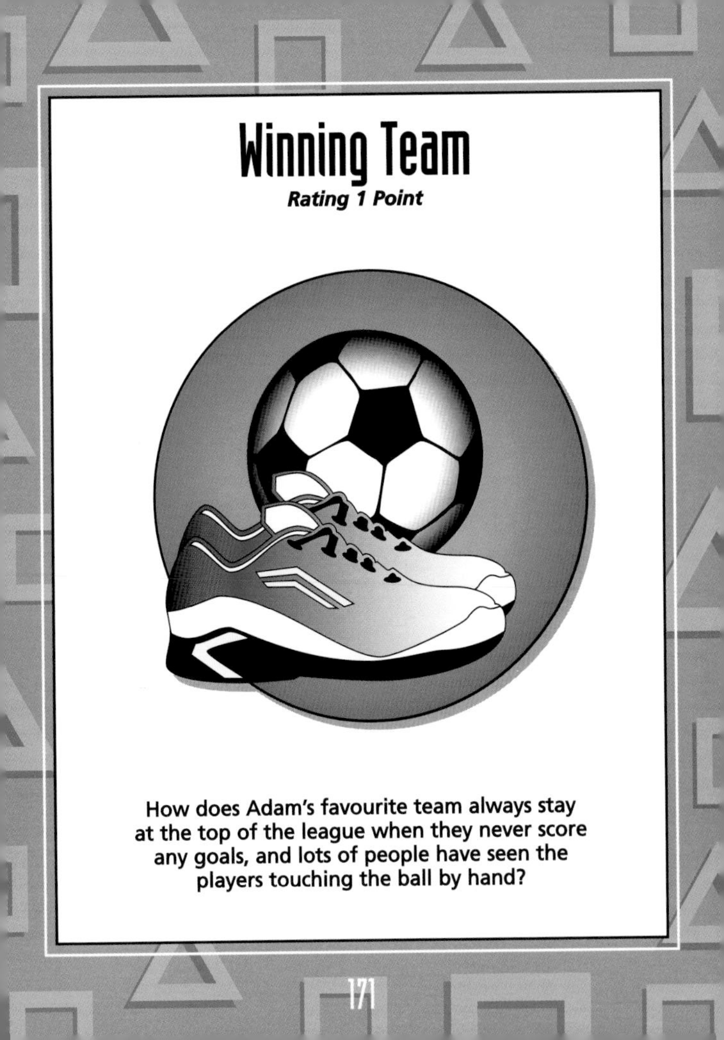

Winning Team

Rating 1 Point

How does Adam's favourite team always stay at the top of the league when they never score any goals, and lots of people have seen the players touching the ball by hand?

Winning Team - Solution

It is a basketball team.

Irish Outrage

Rating 2 Points

Amanda was a passionate spinster who was well known for her conservative views, yet on hearing that O'Reilly had married two women, without divorcing either of them, and with neither woman divorcing him or dying, she was neither shocked or outraged. Why?

Irish Outrage – Solution

O'Reilly was a priest who had
conducted two marriage ceremonies.

Hold Up

Rating 2 Points

A man wearing a black hat and scarf parked outside an expensive jewellers, held up a dozen people and walked out of the shop a couple of minutes later with $1000 worth of jewellery. Although one or two people were peering through the windows of the jewellers at the time, none of them battered an eyelid, and a nearby driver merely gave a honk of his horn. Explain.

Hold Up - Solution

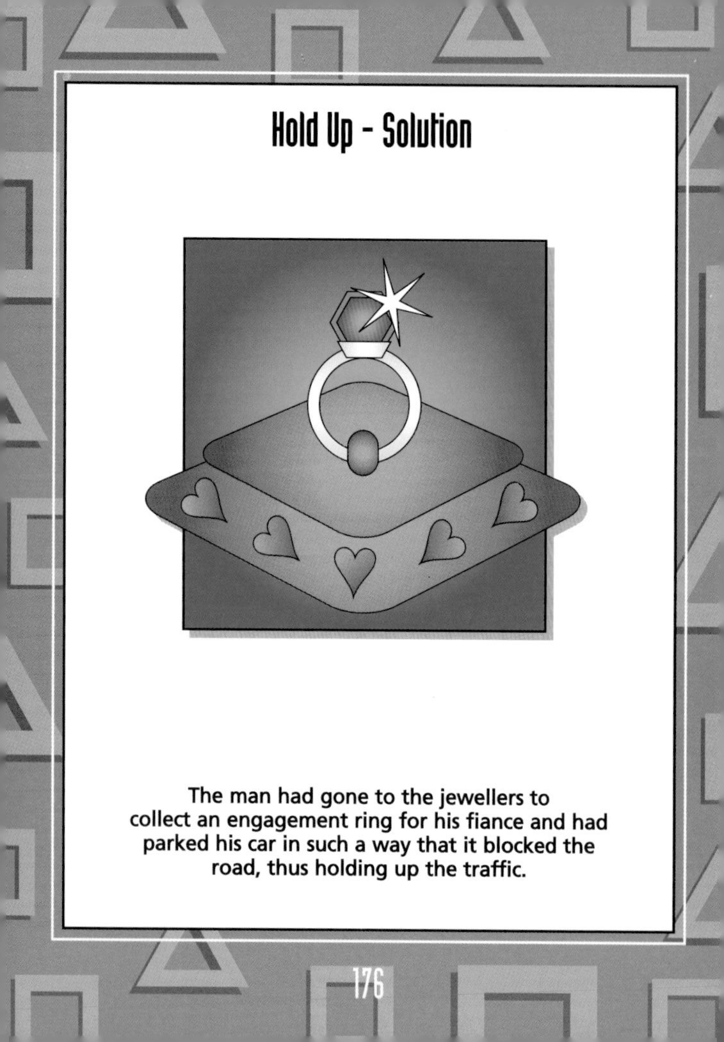

The man had gone to the jewellers to collect an engagement ring for his fiance and had parked his car in such a way that it blocked the road, thus holding up the traffic.

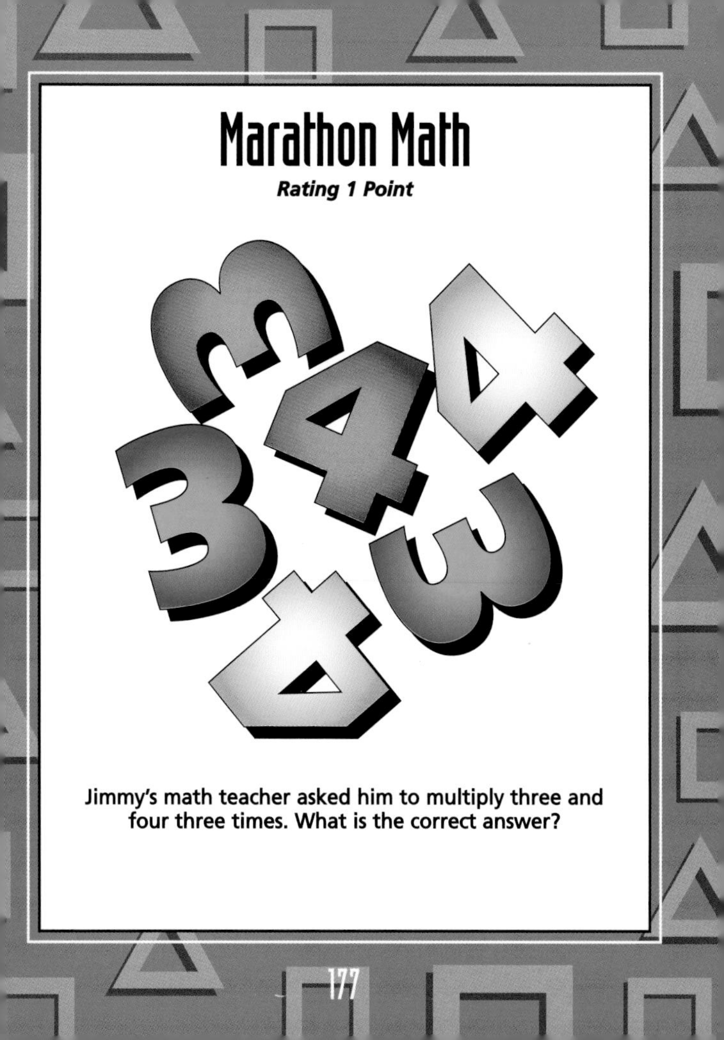

Marathon Math

Rating 1 Point

Jimmy's math teacher asked him to multiply three and four three times. What is the correct answer?

Marathon Math - Solution

Twelve each time.

Speed Racing

Rating 2 Points

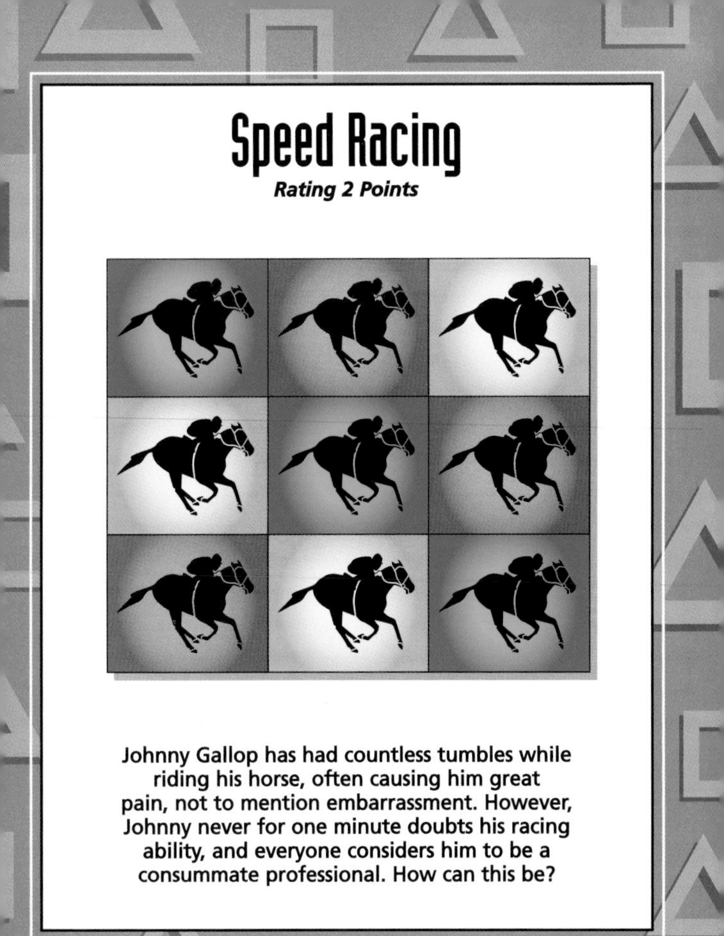

Johnny Gallop has had countless tumbles while riding his horse, often causing him great pain, not to mention embarrassment. However, Johnny never for one minute doubts his racing ability, and everyone considers him to be a consummate professional. How can this be?

Speed Racing – Solution

He is a professional motor racing driver.

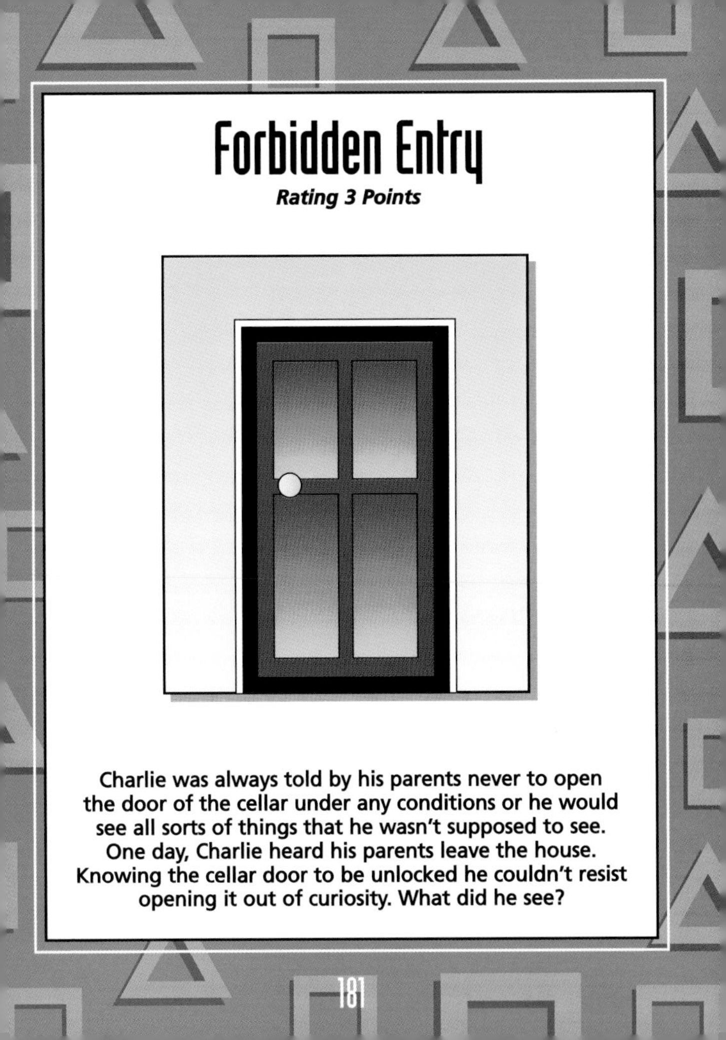

Forbidden Entry

Rating 3 Points

Charlie was always told by his parents never to open the door of the cellar under any conditions or he would see all sorts of things that he wasn't supposed to see. One day, Charlie heard his parents leave the house. Knowing the cellar door to be unlocked he couldn't resist opening it out of curiosity. What did he see?

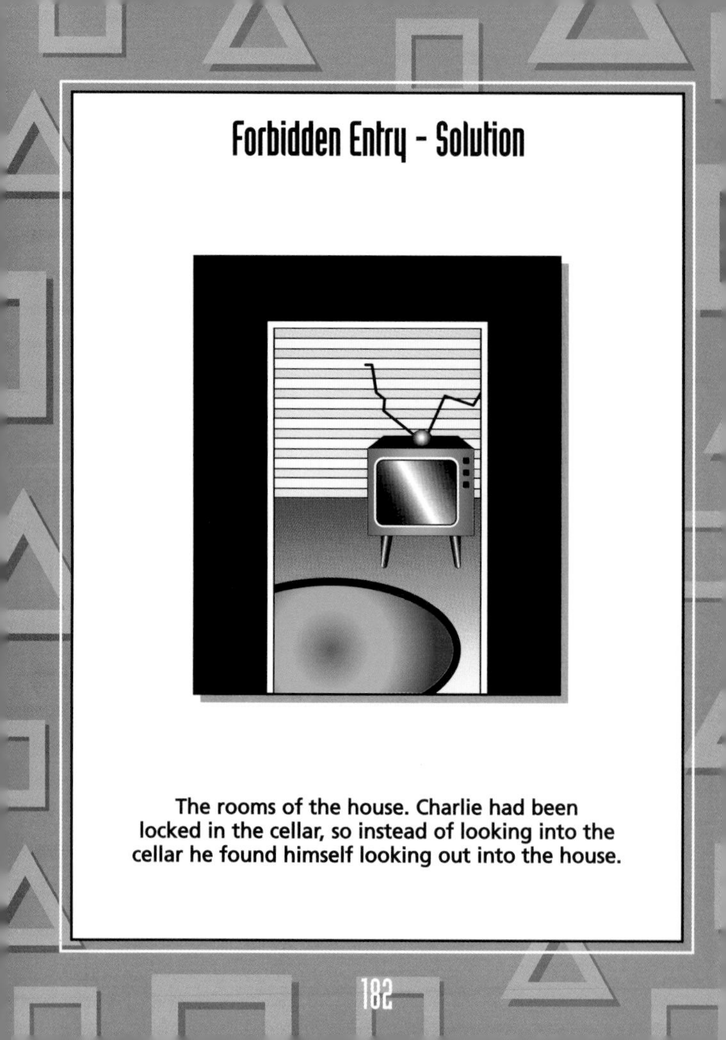

Forbidden Entry - Solution

The rooms of the house. Charlie had been locked in the cellar, so instead of looking into the cellar he found himself looking out into the house.

Broken Journey

Rating 2 Points

Jo Haste and his wife Elaine have taken their electric car on a motoring holiday in France. After driving for five hours one morning, they stop for a gourmet lunch. Afterwards Mr Haste decides to sleep off his glass of red wine, before continuing their journey eastwards towards Lyon. When they set off again – remembering to drive on the left-hand-side of the road – the wind is gusting at 112 km/hour in exactly the opposite direction. In which direction will the car exhaust be blown?

Broken Journey - Solution

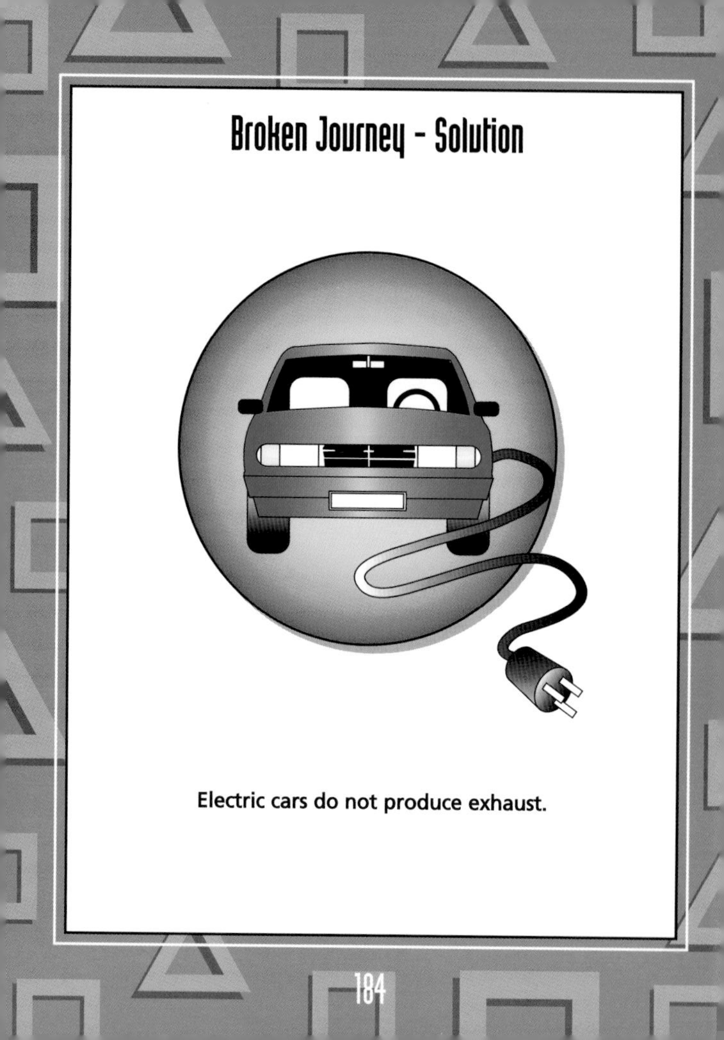

Electric cars do not produce exhaust.

Chance Meeting

Rating 3 Points

Shaun and his best friend, Rick, are watching a tennis tournament. Amongst all the hundreds of fans Shaun happens to spot Rick's brother, Dan. Shaun has only met Dan once before when they were both three months old, and he has seen or heard nothing about him since. How does he instantly know he is looking at Rick's brother?

Chance Meeting – Solution

Because Dan is Rick's identical twin.

Art Form

Rating 2 Points

A man owned an exquisite oil painting known to have been painted by a world famous 17th century Dutch painter. The painting was worth $500,000, yet the man deliberately destroyed it. Why?

Art Form - Solution

The man also owned the only other painting known to be by the same artist. Both paintings were of equal value. By destroying the first painting, the value of the second painting rocketed to over twice its former price.

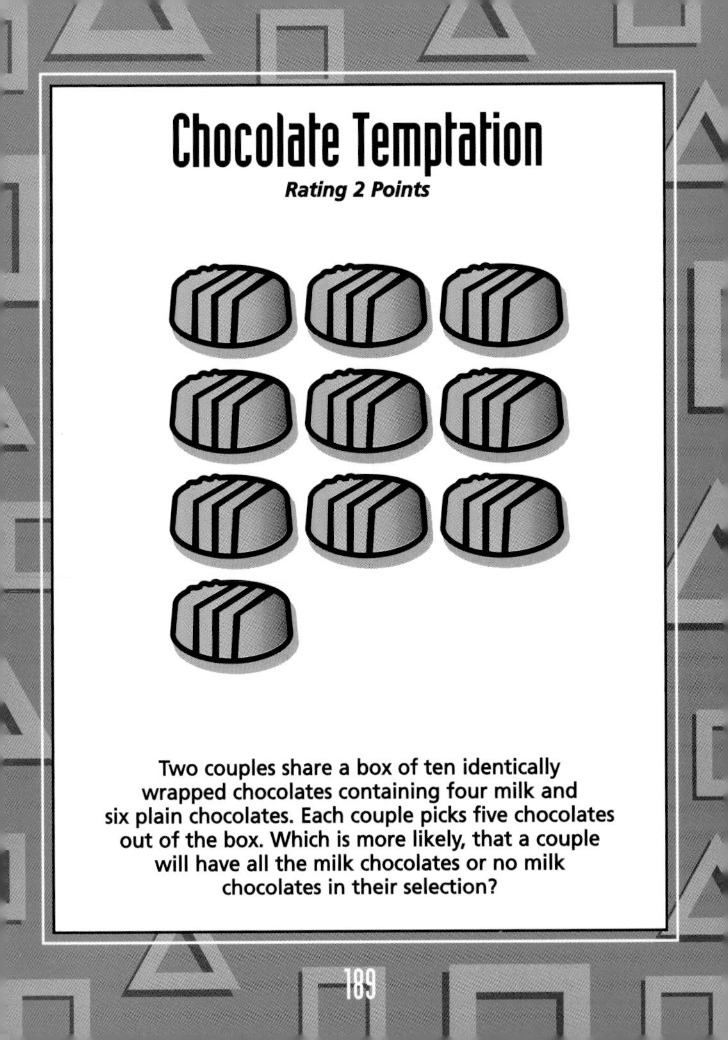

Chocolate Temptation

Rating 2 Points

Two couples share a box of ten identically wrapped chocolates containing four milk and six plain chocolates. Each couple picks five chocolates out of the box. Which is more likely, that a couple will have all the milk chocolates or no milk chocolates in their selection?

Chocolate Temptation - Solution

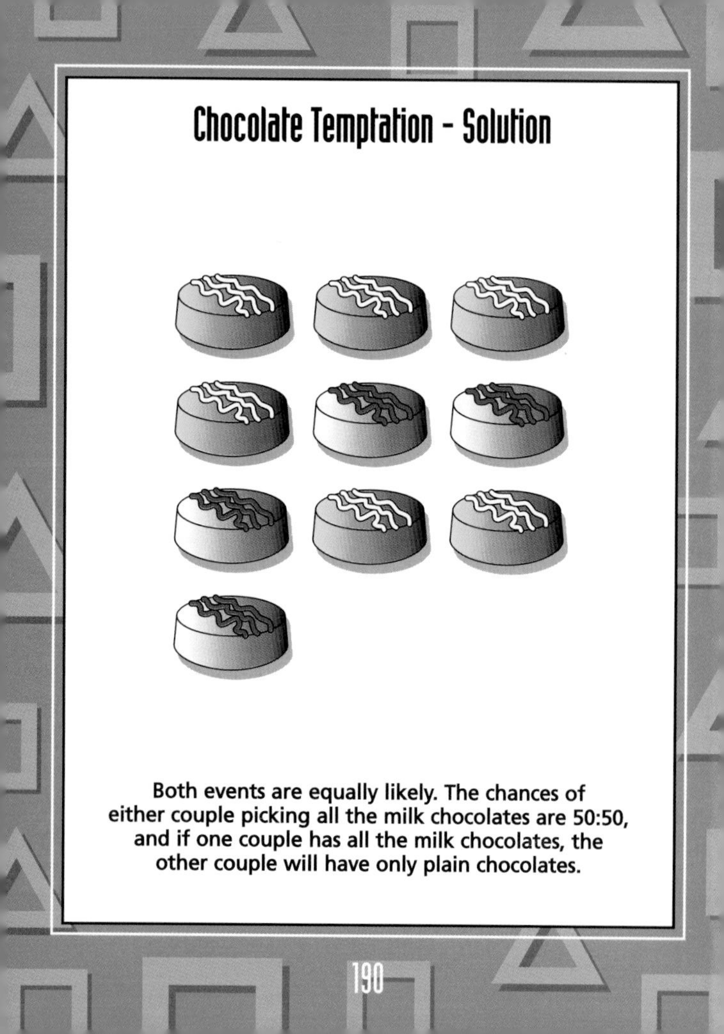

Both events are equally likely. The chances of either couple picking all the milk chocolates are 50:50, and if one couple has all the milk chocolates, the other couple will have only plain chocolates.

Overall Scoring Page

CHAPTER	SCORE CARD	POTENTIAL SCORE	YOUR SCORE
1	Page 8	**40**	______
2	Page 54	**40**	______
3	Page 100	**45**	______
4	Page 146	**45**	______
		GRAND TOTAL	______

Anyone who has scored more than 128 points can safely boast that they can think laterally!

Anyone who got between 85 and 128 points should feel suitably happy having been able to answer more than half the questions correctly.

For those with less than 85 points, turn over to page 192 for more information on Lagoon's other Brain-Boosting and Mind-Bending titles – you need more practice.

OTHER TITLES AVAILABLE FROM LAGOON BOOKS:

BRAIN-BOOSTING PUZZLE BOOKS

BRAIN-BOOSTING VISUAL LOGIC PUZZLES
(ISBN: 1902813200)

BRAIN-BOOSTING CRYPTIC PUZZLES
(ISBN: 1902813219)

MIND-BENDING PUZZLE BOOKS

MIND-BENDING LATERAL THINKING PUZZLES
(ISBN 1899712062)

MORE MIND-BENDING LATERAL THINKING PUZZLES - VOLUME II
(ISBN 1899712194)

MIND-BENDING LATERAL THINKING PUZZLES BY DES MACHALE
(ISBN 1899712232)

MIND-BENDING CONUNDRUMS & PUZZLES
(ISBN 1899712038)

MIND-BENDING CLASSIC LOGIC PUZZLES
(ISBN 1899712186)

MIND-BENDING CLASSIC WORD PUZZLES
(ISBN 1899712054)

MIND-BENDING CROSSWORD PUZZLES
(ISBN 1899712399)

MIND-BENDING CHALLENGING LOGIC PUZZLES
(ISBN 1899712240)

MIND-BENDING CHALLENGING OPTICAL PUZZLES
(ISBN 1899712690)

MIND-BENDING MAZE PUZZLES
(ISBN 1899712720)